LIBERATED ORGASM:
The Orgasmic Revolution

Herbert A. Otto, Ph.D.

LIBERATING CREATIONS, INC.
First, Limited Edition

Liberating Creations, Inc. .
P. O. Box 524
Silverado, California 92676

Copyright 1999, Herbert A. Otto

First edition
Cover design by Judith W. Wood

Library of Congress Cataloging in Publication Data
Otto, Herbert Arthur, 1922-
Liberated Orgasm: A practical guide to enhance sexual pleasure and
the orgasm.
1st edition.
Includes bibliographical references and index.
ISBN 0-9671181-3-1 (pbk.): $23.95
1. Sex instruction. 2. Sexual intercourse 3. Orgasm/climax.
4. Orgasm spectrum extension.

Books by HERBERT A. OTTO, Ph.D.

The Development Of Theory And Practice In Social Casework
(with Nina Garton)

Exploration In Human Potentialities

Ways of Growth
(with John Mann)

Human Potantialities: The Challenge And The Promise

More Joy in Your Marriage

The Family In Search Of A Future

Group Methods To Actualize Human Potential

The New Sexuality

Love Today: A New Exploration

Total Sex
(with Roberta Otto)

Fantasy Encounter Games

Marriage And Family Enrichment—New Perspectives
And Programs

New Life Options—The Working Woman's Resource Book
(with Rosalind Loring)

The New Sex Education

Dimensions In Wholistic Healing
(with James W. Knight)

Letting Go: Uncomplicating Your Life
(with Ramona Adams and Audeane Cowley)

Table of Contents

Introduction and Foreword   **xi**
  A Short History of this Book   xv
Chapter 1—New Light On the Human Orgasm   **1**
  Two Ignored Open Secrets   2
  Background and Goals Of This Study   8
  Orgasm Range Survey   10
  Some Basic Findings   11
  Notes   19

**Chapter 2—Are You Mono-Orgasmic, Poly-Orgasmic
or Hetero-Orgasmic?**
  The Three Core Climatic Groups   21
    The Mono-Orgasmic Person   22
    The Poly-Orgasmic Person   22
    The Hetero-Orgasmic Person   22
    Membership In The Three Core Groups Is Fluid 23
  Orgasm Facts   24
  Resistance To The Liberated Orgasm
  And Other New Sex Findings   26
  The Intercourse And Orgasm Belief Systems   28
  Basic Beliefs About Intercourse   30
  Results Of The Intercourse Belief System Study   33
  Effects Of The Intercourse and Orgasmic Belief System 34
  Notes   40

Chapter 3—The Woman's Basic Seven, Part I   **41**
  Orgasm, Multiple Orgasm And Orgasm Variants   41
    1. The Clitoral Orgasm   45
    What Is The Clitoris And Its Location?   46
    How Important Is The Clitoris?   46
    What Are The Effects Of Clitoral Circumcision? 48
    Psychological Factors Associated With The
    Clitoral Orgasm   49
    How Does A Clitorial Orgasm Feel?   50
    Study Findings   51
    2. The Vaginal/Cervical Orgasm   51
    How Does This Compare With The Clitorial Orgasm? 51

How Does This Orgasm Come About? 52
Does A Vaginal/Cervical Orgasm Always Require A
Man? 54
Psychological Factors Associated With
The Vaginal/Cervical Orgasm 55
Study Findings 56
3. The Breast Orgasm 56
Psychological Factors Associated With
The Breast Orgasm 57
What Women Have To Say About The
Breast Orgasm 58
Study Findings 59
Notes 59

Chapter 4—The Woman's Basic Seven, Part II **61**
4. The Mouth Orgasm 61
Why The Mouth ? 61
Learning About The Mouth Orgasm 62
Psychological Factors Associated With
The Mouth Orgasm 64
How Does A Mouth Orgasm Feel? 64
Study Findings 65
5. The G-Spot Orgasm 66
What Is A G-Spot? Where Is It Located? 66
Who Discovered The G-Spot? 66
Why Do Women Have A G-Spot? 67
How Does The G-Spot Feel When Stimulated? 68
Psychological Factors Associated With The G-Spot 68
More Experiences With The G-Spot 69
What Women Have To Say About The G-Spot
Orgasm 70
Study Findings 71
6. The Anal Orgasm 71
Why The Anus 71
How Does Anal Sex Feel? 72
The Anal Sex Taboo And The Risk Factor
Associated With The Practice 72
Psychological Factors Associated With Anal Sex 73
How Prevalent Is Anal Intercourse
For Women? 74
What Women Have To Say About Anal Orgasms 76
Study Findings 77

7. The Mental Orgasm   77
   How Rare Is It?   77
   Mental Orgasms From External Stimuli   79
   The Inner-directed Mental Orgasm   80
   What Women Say About Their Mental Orgasm   80
   Study Findings   81
   Notes   82
   Resources   82

Chapter 5—The Man's Basic Six   **83**
Male Multiple Orgasms And Variants   83
1. The Penile Orgasm   85
   Understanding The Physiology Of The Penile
   Climax   86
   Psychological Factors Associated With
   The Penile Orgasm   87
   How Men Describe The Penile Orgasm   88
   Study Findings   89
2. The Prostate And Anal Orgasm   89
   Why The Prostate?   90
   Observations About The Prostate Orgasm   91
3. The Anal Orgasm   92
   Psychological Factors Associated With Anal Sex   93
   What Heterosexual Men Have To Say About
   Prostate And Anal Orgasms   95
   Study Findings   95
4. The Breast Orgasm   96
   Why The Breasts?   96
   Psychological Factors Associated With The Male
   Breast Orgasm   97
   How Men Describe The Breast Orgasm   98
   Study Findings   99
5. The Mouth Orgasm   99
   Why The Mouth?   99
   Psychological Factors Associated With The
   Mouth Orgasm   100
   How Men Describe Their Mouth Orgasm   101
   Study Findings   102
6. The Mental Orgasm   102
   How Men Describe Their Mental Orgasms   104
   Study Findings   104
   Notes and Resources   105

**Chapter 6—The Fusion Orgasm, Zone Orgasm,
Lucid Dream Orgasm and More**   **107**
  The Fusion Orgasm   107
    How Does A Fusion Orgasm Feel?   108
    Study Findings   110
  The Zone Orgasm   110
    Study Findings   113
  Dream Orgasms   113
  Lucid Dream Orgasms   114
  The Child's Climax   116
  The Masturbation Climax   117
  The Whole Body Orgasm   119
  Other Types of Peak Ecstasy   120
  Addendum   122
  Notes and Resources   123

**Chapter 7—Orgasmic States Of Being, Orgasm
Shaping And Other Discoveries**   **125**
  The Seven Orgasmic States Of Being   127
    1. Chaotic Ecstacy   127
    2. Fantasy Images   128
    3. Body Focus   128
    4. Intrusive Thoughts   128
    5. Multi-Dimensional Climactic Experiencing   129
    6. Peaceful Orgasmic Experiencing   129
    7. Spiritual Or Transcendental Experiencing And
      Feeling Of Melding Into Oneness   129
  The Discovery Of The Orgasmic States Of Being
  And Orgasmic Shaping: 132
  A Learning Process   132
    Phase 1   132
    Phase 2   133
    Phase 3   134
    Phase 4   134
    Phase 5   136
    The Principal Components Of The Climax   139
    Orgasm Tone—The Added Dimension   141
    Orgasm Body Patterns   142
    The Orgasm Herald   143
    Notes   144

**Chapter 8—New Perspectives On Sex
And The Human Climax**   **145**
  Sex As A Bio-electric Energy Exchange   146

Sexual Lifestyles And Climactic Experiencing 147
The Orgasm Development Programs 150
The Conscious Orgasm Power Shift 152
The Orgasm As A Source Of Health 153
Spiritual Dimensions Of Sex And The Orgasm 155
Sexual Self-Development 161
Notes and Resources 164 & 165
Addendum 165

**Chapter 9—Orgasm Intensification—
A Neglected Art** **167**
The Fundamental Seven Ways 168
  1. Getting Into The Right Position 168
  2. Obtaining Optimum Stimulation 168
  3. Finding The Right Rhythm And Speed 169
  4. Conscious Fantasizing And Visualizing 169
  5. Focusing On Feelings 170
  6. Vocalizing During The Love Act 171
  7. Staying At The Edge 171
Sixteen More Ways of Orgasm Intensification 172
  a. Conscious Tension Induction 172
  b. Influencing The Desire Pattern 172
  c. Changing The Pattern Of Arousal Or Intercourse 173
  d. Total Sensory Immersion 174
  e. Timelessness And Goalessness 175
  f. Innovative Abstinence 175
  g. Environmental Change 175
  h. Genital Exercises 176
  i. The Use Of Alcohol And Drugs 177
  j. The Water Jet Experience 178
  k. Focusing On Love And Caring 179
  l. Orgasm Extension 179
  m. Relaxation Before Sex 179
  n. Breathing Right 180
  o. Exploring Asian Thrust Formulas 180
  p. The Pushout Technique 180
  q. Use Of Sex Toys 181
  Notes 182

**Chapter 10—Methods For Extending The
Liberated Orgasm, Spectrum Part I** **183**
The Developmental Nature Of The Climax: —
"The Orgasm Can Be Shaped" 184

Developing Orgasm Awareness 185
Four Important Elements 185
Guidelines For Extending The Liberated
Orgasm Spectrum 188
The Orgasm Articulation Method 192
Fusion Orgasm Training 193

**Chapter 11—Methods For Extending The
Liberated Orgasm, Spectrum Part II** **197**
The New Pathway Procedure 197
Peak Ecstasy Postponement 202
The Man's Climax Postponement Exercise 202
The Woman's Climax Postponement Extension 204
The Orgasm Tone Experience 204
The Contraction Prolongation Exercise 205
Pre-orgasmic Pleasure Balloon Extension 206
The Orgasmic Diary 208
G-Spot Development—Some Special Considerations 212
Resources 214

**Chapter 12—The Human Orgasm—Exploring The
Further Reaches Of The Possible** **215**
Reflections About The Further Reaches Of
The Orgasm Potential 215
What Really Goes On During The Orgasm? 218
Addendum 222
Notes 222

**Appendix—Human Sexuality: Additional Observations
and Reflections** **223**
A major American Challenge 224
The Great Unacknowledged Scandal In The
Sex Life Of The U.S. 225
The Medical Uses Of Sex As A Healing Agent 225
Creating The First World Museum Of Erotic
Literature And Art 226
Sex Toxicity—A Hidden International Plague 228
A Puzzling Question 229
The Man In The Woman And The Woman In The Man 230
Man, Sex and Society 233
Christianity And Sex 234
What Few Dare Ask Themselves 235

About Non-relational Sex And The Expression
Of Loving Feelings   236
Some Additional Observations   237
Notes   238

Index   **239**

Author's Bibliography—Human Sexuality   **247**

Book Order Form   **249**

INTRODUCTION and FOREWORD

It is evident that through cultural conditioning and the exercise of control, contemporary societies continue to impose restrictions on the sex lives of their members. The social shaping of attitudes about sexual behavior and the enjoyment of sex, by Western societies, is achieved through the implanting of pervasive anxieties, fear, plus shame and guilt about the most intimate form of human relating. As a result, we are highly ambivalent about the recognition, exercise and development of our sexual powers and capabilities.

The Orgasm Spectrum Research Project, with its new findings about the climax, reveals that *the natural human capacities for sexual enjoyment are vastly greater than previously suspected.* These findings pose a challenge and demand change in both perspective and attitudes.

The findings from this work challenge the individual on two levels. First, the sexual belief system is challenged. Men "have always known" they are capable of only the penile orgasm. Most women know "they can only have a clitoral, vaginal/cervical and maybe a G-spot climax."

The second challenge is on an even more deeply personal level. Each person who reads about these findings knows he or she has the *potential* for experiencing a wide range of climaxes and a vastly larger capacity for erotic experiencing than previously suspected. This calls for a decision whether to become engaged in self development to experience an extended range of different types of orgasms, and add new dimensions of peak ecstasy.

The vast majority of men and women will make the decision to "let sleeping dogs lie." Some will rationalize "maybe later on I'll get around to some sexperimentation with this."

All of us have been conditioned by the society in which we live to let very significant aspects of our sexuality remain largely latent and repressed. This applies particularly to the development of the human orgasm.

It is a fact that the findings from this research are disturbing. Opposition, if not antagonism, will be generated. This accounts for my over-a-decade-long struggle to obtain a publisher who has the courage to make this work available to people. Over thirty literary agents turned down this book plus more than fifty major and other publishers.

The liberated orgasm, with its new climax options (plus related discoveries), is often experienced as threatening by women and men. According to some sexologists, close to 40% of the U. S. women never, or rarely, experience an orgasm during intercourse. It is also safe to say that many, if not most, of those women who are orgasmically potent allow themselves to have *only* a clitoral climax.

Many heterosexual males will likely be threatened by the fact that, in addition to the penile (plus zone and fusion) climax, he is capable of and has the option to experience six additional distinct, characteristic, types of orgasms. The woman is capable of seven distinct, characteristic types of orgasms plus the fusion and zone climax. It has been repeatedly demonstrated, for centuries, that the most effective way to suppress new scientific discoveries is by "stonewalling" or ignoring them. The contemporary belief system about the human orgasmic capacity is based on misinformation and misrepresentation. Prominent among the latter is the myth that the woman is capable *only of a clitoral orgasm and the man only of a penile climax.*

These are myths which have largely prevailed since the beginnings of research about human sexuality in the twentieth century and before. This study challenges thoroughly entrenched beliefs about the human climax. It introduces the orgasm revolution, which is already underway. Findings indicate that men and women have vast latent powers and potentials for erotic pleasure and peak ecstasy which are largely suppressed by their sexual belief system.

A SHORT HISTORY OF THIS BOOK

The history of this book clearly reveals contemporary America's love/hate relationship with human sexuality. This book first had the title *New Orgasm Options* which was later changed to *Liberated Orgasm.* Work on this book actually began in 1982. At that time I conducted an initial series of interviews with swingers about their orgasm capabilities and wrote an article— "A New Perspective of the Human Sexual Potential" (unpublished). Other projects intervened until mid-1985 when I began preliminary work on what was to become *Liberated Orgasm.*

Early in 1986, I asked a colleague to join me. Based on my unpublished article about the human sexual potential, we began construction of a questionnaire—"The Orgasmic Range Survey"—to be used for this research. We parted company before this survey was completed. I then totally reworked the survey.

The book was substantially completed early in 1988. In March of that year, I signed a contract with a small New York publisher who specialized in books on human sexuality for sexologists. The publisher promised publication within a year. He told me that the internationally known sexologist, John Money had reviewed the manuscript and recommended its publication. (Subsequently another internationally known sexologist, Dr. Beverly Whipple, also reviewed and endorsed this work.)

The publisher distributed leaflets announcing publication of the book four times between March, 1988 and 1994. No reason was ever given why the book continued to remain unpublished for all these years. In 1994, I sought legal assistance with this matter. After further procrastination, the publisher relinquished the rights to the book in December, 1995.

The help of a skilled editor was obtained and the book was rewritten. This work was completed by the end of October, 1996, when search for an agent and publisher commenced.

After writing to over thirty agents, I found one who liked the manuscript. We then queried over fifty publishers

In January 1999, I asked my companion, Judith W. Wood, to join me in founding Liberating Creations, Inc. in order to make this book available to the public.

ACKNOWLEDGMENTS AND THANKS

I wish to thank the following for their good assistance in the data gathering phase of this work—Dr. James Dedic and Dr. Teresa Rutherford of Cypress College; Professor Pat Elmore of Los Angeles Harbor College; Dr. Leroy J. Cordrey and Dr. Goodhew MacWilliams of California State University, Fullerton, plus Robert and Geri McGinley of Club Wide World and Tom Kilfoyle of Seabreeze Club as well as Frieda Otto Brown, Avery Otto, Cheri Baer and Judith Wood.

Also, thanks for the assistance in data gathering to Benedict Boyd, Director of Programs, Gay and Lesbian Community Service Center of Los Angeles; Werner Kuhn of the Gay and Lesbian Community Services Center of Orange County, and Mark Wedesweiler of the Gay/Lesbian Education Union of California State University, Fullerton.

Thanks for other help and special interviews to Dr. Jerry Hershey of Fullerton Junior College; author Valerie Kelly; therapists Lee B. Teed, Dr. Rachel Copelan, and the late Dr. Paul Bindrim, plus Gary Taylor. Special thanks to my son, H. A. Curt Otto, for his ongoing encouragement plus excellent help and contributions. For ideas and editorial suggestions and other assistance, thanks to Dr. John Money, Dr. Beverly Whipple, Jeanne Pasle-Green, Dr. Alice Ladas.

I am most grateful to sexologist Dr. Suzanne Frayser and especially to Dr. Ray Stubbs for their critical reading and creative suggestions for improvement of the book's first version. In addition I would like to express my thanks to the staff of the Anaheim (California) Public Library. My gratitude also to my agent, Don Congdon, for his hard work and faith in this book.

Finally, thanks also to my former secretary Kris Nelson for her patience, dedication and hard work on the numerous revisions of the first version of the book. The contribution of the editor for this volume, Dr. Natica Greer, needs particular recognition. Her special touches, and humor, as well as her skill for phrasing are very much appreciated.

Thanks to the following for the use of quotations and excerpts from published works—Lonnie Barbach, *For Each Other* (Anchor Press, Doubleday); Alan P. Brauer and Donna Brauer, *ESO—Extended Sexual Orgasm,* (Warner Books); Mantak Chia and Michael Winn, *Taoist Secrets of Love* (Aurora Press); Seymour Fisher, *The Female Orgasm,* (Basic Books); William Hartman and Marilyn Fithian, *Any Man Can* (St. Martin's Press); Stephen LaBerge, *Lucid Dreaming* (Ballantine Books); Alice K. Ladas, Beverly Whipple and John Perry, *The G-Spot* (Holt, Rinehart and Winston); William Masters, Virginia Johnson and Robert Kolodny, *Sex and Human Loving* (Little, Brown & Company); Margaret Mead, *Male and Female,* (William Morrow); Mark Meshorer and Judith Meshorer, *Ultimate Pleasure* (St. Martin's Press); Paul Pearsall, *Sexual Healing* (Crown Publishers); Josephine L. Sevely, *Eve's Secrets* (Random House); Steve Sovatsky, *Eros As Mystery;* Paul Tabori, *The Humor And Technology of Sex* (Julian Press); *Forum International; Archives of Sexual Behavior; Journal of Sex Education and Sex Therapy; Journal of Sex and Marital Therapy; Journal of Sex Research; Playboy , Penthouse* and *Time* magazines.

CHAPTER 1

NEW LIGHT ON THE HUMAN ORGASM

It seems auspicious that a new perspective and understanding of sex and the human orgasm is becoming available at this particular time—the dawn of the 21st century. Americans and other people in the world are on the very cusp of a massive change in their attitudes, perspectives and the underlying emotional forces which determine the experience of sex.

In December, 1993, a *Cosmopolitan* magazine article was published entitled "The Truth About Female Ejaculation." This is the first sentence of the article: "These days, nobody splutters into their soup if you mention the word 'orgasm' at the dinner table." The orgasm, has not only come out of the closet, but has begun to be liberated. Liberated in the sense that formerly hidden or unknown orgasmic options are now understood and can be freely pursued. We are in the beginnings of what can be called, "the orgasmic revolution." This is the first book exclusively devoted to the whole range of dynamics, possibilities and potentials involved in the human climax.

The research published in this volume challenges widespread misinformation and thoroughly entrenched false beliefs about the human climax. This is an investigation of the human orgasmic potential, i.e., the psychological factors and body components which stimulate and trigger the climax in men and women and what this experience means, plus how it feels to them. Study findings clearly indicate that both men and women have vastly greater sexual powers—as well as the ability to experience various types of peak ecstasy—than previously suspected. The big news is that *the orgasm can be*

1

formed, developed or shaped. This involves a creative process which can be learned. The findings from this study will significantly expand the human potential for sexual pleasure, which has been vastly underestimated.

The orgasm is already being discussed both socially and intimately among lovers. A whole new framework for understanding this peak event has now emerged. It furnishes a map for use in exploring the vast inner universe of the human climax which has remained largely hidden. Use of the map will deepen communication and the level of intimacy among lovers. It also offers an adventure in the exploration and development of new climactic feeling tones as well as the experiencing of new types of orgasms.

What many have been calling, "the greatest pleasure in life," is now revealed to conceal a multitude of options. Peak ecstasy, for example, is a gateway to increased self-knowledge. Sex and the orgasm also offer options for transcendental or spiritual experiencing as well as mystical communion. The early explosive growth of the as yet largely unacknowledged U. S. spiritual sex movement clearly indicates one of the major trends of tomorrow. In short, the human climax has emerged as a key energy matrix in the human personality which offers new erotic pleasure and whose potentials have just begun to be known.

TWO IGNORED OPEN SECRETS

Cultural anthropologist, Margaret Mead, reached an interesting conclusion in her key book entitled, *Male and Female: A Study of Sexes In A Changing World,* published almost fifty years ago. She states: "There seems, therefore, to be a reasonable basis for assuming that the human female's capacity for orgasm is to be viewed much more as a *potentiality that may or may not be developed by a given culture.*" (1) Emphasis added.

The late Margaret Mead did not take her conclusion far enough—*it is not only the female's but also the male's ca-*

*pacity for orgasmic response, over and beyond the penile or-
gasm, which exists as a potentiality that may or may not be
developed by a given culture.* Mead's observation (as expanded)
applies to all contemporary cultures. The culture, or society,
largely determines the individual's sexual belief system as well
as his or her spectrum of sexual experiencing and types of
orgasms.

The new findings of this study significantly expand our
understanding of peak sexual ecstasy. Their major contribution will be to demolish the belief system about peak sex entrenched since the beginnings of history. The male especially
will profit as he has been conditioned to believe he is capable
only of the penile orgasm. Actually he has the potential to
experience six discrete or characteristic climaxes, the woman
seven. In addition, both genders are also capable of having a
fusion and a zone orgasm.

Sexologists Ladas, Perry and Whipple distinguish between a *climax* and an *orgasm.* The latter involves involuntary contractions over the entire body. (2) It is my observation
that women's climaxes vary so idiosyncratically in their physiological (and psychological) manifestations that such a dis-
tinction does not appear to be justified. Throughout this volume, therefore, the terms "orgasm" and "climax" are used interchangeably.

Most sexologists have concluded that sex is largely a
learned response. Not only are most of our sexual behavior
and response patterns learned, but *the orgasm as well as the
possibilities of this event, are also learned.* The implication is
that what is learned is furnished by the society in which we
grow up. The question has to be asked: "What is the content
of the learning about sex which defines the parameters of a
person's sexual potential?" In the United States, particularly,
the learning content about sex is essentially based on information provided by the field of sexology and sex education.

Due to the growing emphasis in this country on equal
rights, individualism and personal freedom, there has been
an increasingly open dissemination of sexual information over
the past thirty years. This period had its beginnings with the
release of the Kinsey Report. Since then, the relatively free

3

flow of sexual information has continued to enrich the sex lives of members of this society. Despite the efforts to reverse this by several successive politically conservative administrations, a climate of sexual liberalism has largely been preserved. For example:

- The U. S. population has never been more tolerant of people's differing sexual life styles. Although there have been temporary setbacks, sexual bigotry is at an all time high.
- A U. S. government study released in the nineties reveals that better than 80 percent of women have premarital sex, with the number continuing to rise.
- The incidence (and acceptance) of oral sex and other formerly frowned upon sex practices has increased dramatically over the past fifteen years.
- Since the Kinsey Report there has been at least a doubling in the weekly frequency of intercourse, while the length of sexual intercourse has, according to some sexologists, more than doubled.
- The number of women who have not yet had an orgasm either by themselves and/or during intercourse, appears to be declining. Conversely, the number of multi-orgasmic women is rising.

It is evident that the U. S. population is now enjoying sex more than ever before. However, considerable sexual suffering and gender discrimination remains. Sexual misinformation and lack of information is widespread. *A deep-seated ambivalence about human sexuality continues to persist in America.*

This country appears to lead the world in the area of sex education for public school students and on the college level. It is also a major contender for leadership in having made numerous, valuable contributions to our understanding of human sexuality. Undoubtedly more sex research has been done and more books on sex have been published in this nation than anywhere else in the world. At the same time, the U. S. continues to be engaged in a massive love/hate relationship with sex.

4

A major hallmark of this ambivalence, is that as of this writing, there is no endowed chair in sexology at any major college or university in America. Hopefully, in the first part of the new millennium, this unbelievable gap will be filled by a perceptive, intelligent donor who has the vision and courage to acknowledge the important contribution sex research is making and can make to the species.

Over the past fifteen years, sexologists have become increasingly aware that the human capacity for orgasmic experiencing is much more extensive than previously suspected. Many sexologists and very large segments of the public continue to believe that only "the historic three" orgasms are possible. These are the clitoral, vaginal and penile climaxes. These are myths which exert a form of social control and they are harmful and pernicious. These myths control the sexual behavior of populations not only in the U. S., but all over the world, by limiting the sexual experiencing of people everywhere.

The fact is that both genders are capable of experiencing a very considerable range, or spectrum, of unique, characteristic climaxes. *This is the most ignored first open secret about human sexual functioning.* Within the past years, a growing number of sexologists, (A. Ladas, B. Whipple, J. Perry, S. Hite, etc.) in their publications have referred to the existence of types of orgasms other than the classical three. For decades, the editors of such magazines as *Penthouse*, *Playboy* and *Penthouse Forum*, who use sexologists as consultants, have referred to the existence of numerous types of orgasms.

For example: in a letter from a reader which appeared in the January 1984 edition of *Playboy* magazine, a man writes that he and his girlfriend decided to experiment by trying to bring her to orgasm *by nipple stimulation only.* After ten minutes, she had an orgasm and reacted the way she does when she has a vaginal orgasm. The *Playboy* Advisor commented as follows: *"Many women are capable of experiencing orgasm without clitoral (or vaginal) stimulation. We've heard of women who could be stimulated on the ear lobe."* (Emphasis added.) Two other letters appear below.

To the *Playboy* Advisor:
"The other night, my wife turned the tables on me. She sucked my nipples the way she likes it done to her, and she was able to bring me to orgasm without even touching my penis. Is this normal for a guy?"

The *Playboy* Advisor responds (December, 1994):
"Tat-for-tit, we always say. It's infrequent, but it is normal. Many men love to have their nipples caressed, and sex researchers are still looking for the man whose nipples don't become erect just before orgasm."

Letter to the *Penthouse Forum:*
"I love performing fellatio on my boyfriend as much as possible, and I love bringing him to orgasm this way and then swallowing his semen. Recently during one of these sessions, I was really into it and was turned on tremendously. My throat started contracting and throbbing, and I started seeing stars. *I had what I believe was an oral orgasm.* It was quite similar to a regular orgasm, except all of the sensations were concentrated in my throat and head." (Emphasis added.)

The *Penthouse Forum* Advisor responds (November, 1982 issue:
"Your experience confirms the fact that *women can have many kinds of orgasms due to the stimulation of many erotic areas of the body.* Breast stimulation, clitoral manipulation, vaginal penetration and even fantasy alone have all been known to produce orgasm in women." (Emphasis added.)

The fact that the man and woman have a vast capacity to experience different and unique orgasms while using various parts of the human anatomy to trigger the climax, remains largely unknown. The human orgasm is the result of a large number of complex forces and components which we are only beginning to understand (see also Chapter 7, pp. 132-139).

Many of these forces can be consciously and willfully altered, or strengthened to enhance the climax. The orgasm is not merely a reflex process. In short, *the human climax, regardless of source, is developmental in nature.* It is an event which can be influenced, molded and shaped. *This is the second ignored open secret.*

Aside from the data obtained as a result of this study, there is a great deal of corroborative evidence that the human orgasm can, to a considerable extent, be formed or developed (see, for example, Chapters 6, 7, 8, and 9).

- Western (and Eastern) couples have known for many decades that the intensity of the climax can be increased by using a variety of ways and means. (See Chapter 9, pp. 168-181). This is the largest recent collection and contains 23 such ways.)

- Since the nineteenth and twentieth centuries (and before), the European erotic and sexual literature has included descriptions of various types of orgasms, how they felt and what triggered these types in both men and women. The same can be said of Oriental erotic literature, "pillow books," etc. About seven years ago, a new, now flourishing genre of books was initiated by U. S. publishers. Called "erotic literature," or "erotica," these volumes describe in detail a wide variety of orgasms similar to those described in subsequent chapters.

- Certain herbs, chemicals or drugs (as well as alcohol), when ingested, affect the climax. This varies with the dosage used and the individual. In numerous interviews, people have reported that LSD and marijuana especially have brought changes to their *orgasmic experiencing.* The next three decades will see considerable experimentation in this area by people, as well as scientists, plus the creation of new chemical and herbal substances to enhance peak ecstasy.

- Current training programs in Tantric Sex rituals (India) and Taoist sex (China) are offered in many parts of the U. S. (see Chapter 8, pp. 158-159). These programs assist trainees to achieve characteristic types of orgasms unique to each of these disciplines. *They are, in effect, teaching orgasm shaping.*

- The *lucid dream orgasm* (Chapter 6, p. 114), achievable through training, offers the trainee a smorgasbord of orgasms from which to choose while asleep.

BACKGROUND AND GOALS OF THIS STUDY

My interest in the human orgasm dates back to the late seventies and early eighties. In 1981, I conducted an initial series of interviews about people's orgasmic experiences, for the most part with members of "swing" clubs. My rationale was that "swingers" were quite likely the most sexually active segment of the U. S. population. As such, they were also likely to be more sexually experimental, using various ways to reach the climax.

These interviews yielded an initial series of discoveries. Based on these, in July 1982, I then wrote an article entitled "A New Perspective of the Human Sexual Potential." Despite its errors and shortcomings, much of the theoretical framework on which this volume is based was first stated in this manuscript. The article was submitted for publication and rejected. Other interests intervened, until February 1985, when concentrated work was begun on the Orgasm Spectrum Research Project. It was clear that an auspicious time had arrived to complete this work.

A major focus of this initial study was to explore and describe the range or types of orgasms experienced by men and women. A phenomenological approach was utilized, i.e. reports of the human orgasmic experiences by a wide range of participants was used as the primary source of data. This approach to the understanding of the human orgasm is based on the assumption that people's subjective reports of the climactic experience are of value in understanding what takes place during peak ecstasy. This appears to be the first such extensive, in-depth study utilizing both hetero and homosexual men and women as subjects.

It was the purpose of this initial exploratory research to seek answers to the following questions:

1. What are the unique characteristics of the woman's range of orgasms?

2. What are the unique characteristics of the man's range of orgasms?

3. What are the physiological and psychological components of the various type of orgasmic experiences?

4. What is the nature and range of the extended human orgasm spectrum?

5. *What are the implications and applications of findings from this study to the sex life of men and women?*

In short, it was the major objective of this research to study the variety of orgasms, reported by men and women, in order to learn more about the nature of the climax and the human orgasmic potential. *It was not the intent of this study to determine the extent to which particular types of orgasms were reported by various segments of the American population.*

A total of 513 individuals participated in the research; 335 participants, called the Primary Group, filled in the Orgasmic Range Survey, a questionnaire especially designed for this study. This is an initial and fundamentally explorative research project. Of the participants, 205 were women and 130 men. Participants were drawn from three sources—college students, "swingers." and the general population. Largely youthful, the vast majority had attended college for several years. Over 300 interviews were conducted.

9

The sexual preference of the Primary Group was as follows - of the 205 women 182, (88%) identified themselves as heterosexual; 18 (10%) stated they were bi-sexual and 6, (3%) said they were lesbian. Of the 130 men 113 (87%) identified themselves as heterosexual; 4, (3%) indicated they were bi-sexual and 13, (10%) said they were homosexual.

As previously mentioned, a first series of interviews of heterosexuals was conducted in 1982. It indicated that among highly sexually active men and women, or "swingers," there were more individuals who had experienced orgasms other than the historic three (the penile, clitoral and vaginal) than those from the general population. For this reason an effort was made to obtain "swingers" as respondents for the project. (Numerically they constitute a small minority.)

A study of married swingers by Richard J. Jenks, published in 1985, sheds interesting light on this highly sexually active segment of the U. S. population. According to this study, the majority of swingers were white and had above average levels of both education and income. Approximately two thirds were 28-45 years of age. The majority identified with some religious organization and were members of the middle class. The plurality were moderate in philosophy and voted Republican. (3)

THE ORGASM RANGE SURVEY

The survey contains the following definition used throughout this study:

Orgasm is defined as the climactic pleasure occurring at the peak of stimulation, involving feelings of physio-psychological release (and ecstatic pleasure)* usually accompanied by rhythmic muscular contractions. The beginnings of an orgasm may occur in specific body parts and may then expand from there, giving the orgasm an unique and characteristic quality.

* In 1998 I added the words in parenthesis to this definition.

It should be noted that regardless of definition, on approaching an orgasm, an increase in breathing, heart-rate and muscular tension can usually be observed.

Sexologists employ a variety of definitions to describe the human orgasm. According to Masters and Johnson, for example, if, in the woman's orgasm, there is no contraction of the genitals, it is not an orgasm. Yet some women reach a peak in their sexual tension, followed by release and relaxation *without observing any genital contractions.*

Other sexologists insist than an orgasm involves a "total body response." Again, this work has revealed that there are some women who report experiencing an orgasmic release with only a very slight or no apparent body response. Such a response may occur in the upper body parts, or hips or torso, for example. It may involve only a limited number of mild contractions, or no apparent contractions at all. The fact is that the physio-psychological manifestations of the female orgasm vary widely.

Forty-eight persons filled in the Orgasmic States of Being Survey and thirty completed the Intercourse Belief System Questionnaire, both of which were developed for this project. Finally, a separate study, involving 100 members of the gay community was conducted. The majority of all participants in the Orgasm Spectrum Research Project were comparatively young (under forty) and better educated than most, with 87% of the women and 88% of the men having one or more years of college. Of this number, 25% were college graduates or had advanced degrees.

SOME BASIC FINDINGS

Until the Orgasm Spectrum Research Project was completed, the parameters of the man's and woman's orgasmic potential had remained largely unknown. *This work established the first comprehensive taxonomy, or definitive classification of the human orgasm.* A framework is now available which sheds new light on our understanding of the human capacity to experience peak ecstasy. *Both genders are capable of a very rich spectrum of orgasms.* As has been previously mentioned, the man is capable of experiencing six distinct types of orgasms, the woman seven, plus both can experience the zone and fusion orgasms.

The following table summarizes the range of different peak ecstasy types, the orgasm spectrum which men and women are able to experience.

THE HUMAN CAPACITY TO EXPERIENCE DIFFERENT TYPES OF ORGASMS: THE ORGASM SPECTRUM

Type of Orgasm	Capacity to Experience	
	Women	Men
1) The Clitoral Orgasm	X	
2) The Vaginal/Cervical Orgasm	X	
3) The Breast Orgasm	X	X
4) The Mouth Orgasm	X	X
5) The G-Spot Orgasm	X	
6) The Prostate Orgasm		X
7) The Anal Orgasm	X	X
8) The Penile Orgasm		X
9) The Mental Orgasm	X	X

Note: The zone and fusion orgasms are also capable of being achieved by both men and women (see Chapter 6)

This orgasm spectrum offers a multiplicity of choices—thus liberating the orgasm. By opening this cornucopia of climaxes, it is not the intent to add new performance pressures, or to define unattainable goals. Nor is it the aim to raise unrealistic hopes about the orgasmic experience. This framework for the understanding of orgasms also is not intended as a hierarchic classification. One type of climax is not superior to another. Nor does having several types of orgasms make one person superior to another individual who greatly enjoys only one type.

Most of us have *a hierarchic tendency—that is, we have a tendency to use a system which ranks things or persons one above the other.* Use of this tendency, vis-a-vis our new understanding of the orgasm, builds a trap. We need to avoid forms of order such as this is "the best" climax, that is the "second best," etc.

Erecting such orgasm hierarchies is most unfortunate. *It keeps us from appreciating that orgasms differ from each other.* Each has its own characteristics and feeling tones and needs to be appreciated for its uniqueness. Attempts to rank your climactic spectrum results in closing yourself to the richness of each climax and its various dimensions. As your sensitivity increases, each orgasm can be recognized as one-of-a-kind—a magic moment.

The orgasm is a very private experience. It is also rich in possibilities because essentially a person creates his or her own climaxes. The individual's own initiative and willful application can play an important role in the development of the climax. Indications are that the autonomous nervous system contributes about 25% (or less) to the process we call the human orgasm, with the mind and emotional factors providing 75%.

A number of astonishing, startling and in some ways "hard to believe" new perspectives and findings about the human orgasmic event have emerged as a result of this exploratory research. They are briefly summarized here, and will be covered in greater detail in subsequent chapters.

A. Although the majority of the participants in the study stated that their orgasms generally "feel the same," a considerable number of people (possibly as high as 20-25% of the general population) in addition to the clitoral, vaginal or penile climax, seem to be able to experience a number of other types of orgasms.

B. For the first time, as a result of this study, the man and woman's *potential* for climactic experiencing has been clearly outlined. By providing this new information, *new climactic options become possible, thus liberating the orgasm.* It is evident that the vast majority of humanity is functioning at about less than 5% of their sexual potential.

C. Analysis of the verbal or written descriptions of the women's Basic Seven orgasms (and the man's Basic Six) revealed that none had a particular pattern of climactic descriptions. Women's descriptions of their clitoral orgasms, for example, showed no major similarities. Men's descriptions of their penile orgasms showed no major similarities, etc. Each orgasm appears to be a highly unique, individualistic or idiosyncratic event.

D. The new framework for understanding the capacity to experience peak ecstasy is an initial effort. It can be expected to make a contribution by encouraging people to increasingly explore the boundaries of their erotic experiencing, while at the same time significantly expanding the spectrum or range of their sexual pleasure. Hopefully, this work will also stimulate further research.

E. It is now evident that the human sexual nervous system extends considerably beyond the genitalia. The sexual nervous system of the woman includes the following Basic Seven sources of orgasm: the clitoris, the vaginal/cervical complex, the G-Spot, the anus, the breasts, the mouth and the mental orgasm. The sexual nervous system of the man includes the following Basic Six sources of orgasm: the penis, the prostate, the anus, the breasts, the mouth and the mental orgasm. In addition, both genders are also capable of a fusion and zone orgasm. Since men as well as women are also able to have a *mental orgasm,* there is a need to expand the definition of the "human sexual nervous system." The psyche or mind needs to be included as a part of the sexual nervous system. This has long been acknowledged by vox populi—"Sex is mostly in the mind."

F. The human orgasm is a vastly more complex phenomenon than previously envisioned. As a subjective experience, the climax can have multiple layers of "dimensionality," or orgasmic states of being. For example, a person who

14

chooses to focus on the nature of the orgasmic flow (thereby acquiring orgasm awareness) can learn to differentiate a number of changes involving feelings, plus fantasies or images, which take place during this process. It is possible to sense the unique characteristics of a climax due to it's being triggered by a specific component(s) of the sexual nervous system, while, at the same time, being aware of *orgasmic states of being* (see Chapter 7, pp. 127-130).

G. As previously mentioned, the climax is not "merely an autonomous nervous system discharge," or "a monolithic entity, or reflex, which is totally beyond the control of the individual." The human orgasm is *developmental*—it can, to a considerable extent, be formed or shaped. For example, the sexual nervous system component which, for many people, imparts a unique characteristic to the climax can be varied. In addition, the character or feeling tone of the climax itself can be altered by a variety of means such as changing its intensity and quality, introducing *orgasm tone*, utilizing a blended or fusion orgasm, etc. (Chapters 7, 11, 12). The human orgasm is, in actuality, a "moveable feast" which can be enriched and enhanced.

H. The *zone orgasm* was discovered at the mid-point of this study (Chapter 6, p.110). Numerous people are able to have an orgasm solely from stimulation or kissing of a zone such as at the side of the neck, the ears, etc. The implications of this orgasm are manifold. Among the most important: 1) emotional factors appear to play a more major role in the human climax than previously suspected, 2) this type of orgasm may be a key to a much deeper understanding of the dynamics involved in the human climax, with more research needed.

I. The new data from this study is supportive of the *whole body orgasm* concept which, in recent years, has fueled increasing interest. *Whole body orgasm in the sense that, for some individuals, the orgasm is no longer genitally cen-*

15

tered but has spread to other body parts and usually the whole body. An understanding of the forces involved in this process awaits further investigation. (See Chapter 3, p. 43.)

J. The component of the sexual nervous system (clitoris, G-Spot, penis, prostate, etc.) which is utilized as a trigger in the induction of the orgasm, for many individuals, contributes a unique quality, giving the climax its particular characteristics. *(They are called "trigger component attributes.")*

K. *Orgasm discrimination,* or the capacity for distinguishing between the various types of climaxes which are obtained from different trigger sources of the sexual nervous system, can be either spontaneously acquired or *learned.* Eight methods, or means, which will foster orgasm discrimination, have been developed and identified (See Chapter 10, pp. 190-192).

L. It is now clear that the *mental orgasm* originally noted by Kinsey, consists of two types: the externally triggered climax and the inner directed orgasm. Kinsey thought that only women could have this orgasm. *We now know that men also have this capacity.*

M. Every person who has orgasms is a member of one of three core groups. He or she is either *mono-orgasmic,* (has an orgasm from stimulation of one component of the sexual nervous system), or p*oly-orgasmic* (can have a climax from stimulation of more than one component of the sexual nervous system). *Members of these first two groups report that all orgasms feel substantially the same.* Finally, the person may be *hetero-orgasmic.* He or she can have a climax from stimulation of more than one component of the sexual nervous system—*yet each climax has unique and distinct characteristics imparted by the component which triggers the orgasm.* The three Core Climactic groups will be discussed in detail in the next chapter.

16

N. From this study emerged the first comprehensive taxonomy—or definitive classification—of the human orgasm.
It provides new knowledge and perspectives of the climax
and furnishes a firm basis for further research.

The findings from this initial, exploratory Orgasm Spectrum Research Project have additional major implications:

1. The field of sex education, which largely creates the belief
system about human sexuality in Western societies, is especially challenged by the new findings about the orgasm. Sex
education is now offered an unprecedented opportunity to help
people experience a richer, more variegated spectrum of climactic experiencing—in short, to enjoy sex more.

There has been an excessive emphasis on the providing of information in sex education classes. Hopefully, while
providing this new information about the liberated orgasm, a
new thrust will begin to emerge. This is the focus on the maximum use of one of the most effective components in the teaching process—*feelings and emotions of students need to be maxi-
mally utilized in the learning process.* There needs to be more
clarification of the important role of emotions during sex, and
that these need to be communicated.

As never before, sex education is faced with the possibility of helping people to actualize more of their sexual potential by assisting the individual to become aware of the options inherent in the extended orgasm spectrum and the developmental nature of the human climax. Sex education needs
to focus more clearly on sexual self-development (Chapter 8,
pp.161-163).

2. The concept of the liberated orgasm and related findings
have numerous implications for sex therapy programs. A
series of options and alternatives, not previously available
to treatment programs concerned with sexual dysfunction,
can now be utilized. Much guilt, confusion and dysfunction based on misinformation can now be more expedi-
tiously dealt with.

3. Sexual rehabilitation programs (especially those for para- and quadriplegics), can utilize findings from this work to construct training programs designed to bring about new levels of orgasmic satisfaction and sexual pleasure for the disabled.

4. We are faced with the abolition of the straight-jacket of "clitorocentrism" (the erroneous belief that all of the woman's climaxes are traceable to the clitoris) plus the old paradigm of the historic woman's three orgasms and the myth that men can only have a penile climax. This opens numerous new avenues and directions for sex research.

5. Finally, the findings from this work have implications for fostering and expanding the level of sexual freedom for all people.

The knowledge of having a larger number of sexual options than previously imagined, generally appears to have a freeing or liberating effect on a person. Increased freedom is related to the discovery that one has more options or choices than previously imagined. As Roger Rosenblatt so well summarized what is clearly the key issue in any definition of freedom: "for thousands of years, various, and very different definitions of freedom—Aristotelian, Cortesian, Augustinian, Kantian—*have all related freedom to significant choice.*" (4) Emphasis added.

Knowing of potential capacities that can be developed as a matter of choice contributes an element of hope. Although specific sexual potentials may, for various reasons, never be actualized, *the individual benefits from a clear awareness of having the possibility, or choice, of expanding the horizon of his or her abilities to experience sexual pleasure.* Having the *knowledge* about attaining increased sexual pleasure and having the choice of developing the capacities to do so, can increase the sense of freedom and stimulate hope, the sense of adventure and *joie de vivre.*

18

Notes

1. Margaret Mead, *Male and Female*, (William Morrow, 1947) : 217

2. Alice K. Ladas, Beverly Whipple and John D. Perry, *The G-Spot*, (Holt, Rinehart and Winston), 1982.

3. Richard J. Jenks, "Swinging: A Replication and Test of a Theory," *Journal of Sex Research*, 2 (1985): 199-205.

4. Roger Rosenblatt, "The Freedom of the Damned," *Time Magazine*, October 6, 1986: 98.

CHAPTER 2

ARE YOU MONO-ORGASMIC, POLY-ORGASMIC OR HETERO-ORGASMIC?

Everyone who experiences an orgasm is a member of one of the *three basic climatic groups,* discovered in the course of this study. This is discussed in the first part of this chapter. The next section contains a variety of interesting orgasm facts not generally known.

Why do many people feel a strong resistance to the concept of the liberated orgasm and other new sex findings? Some answers to this question are provided in the next to last section. The final section of this chapter explores a much neglected area—the role of the intercourse and orgasm belief systems which play an important role in our sex lives.

The Three Core Climactic Groups

Among today's sexually active population, there is a group of individuals who are variously described as *anorgasmic* or *pre-orgasmic.* They have not yet attained an orgasm. This group is predominantly composed of women. Excluding those who have not yet experienced an orgasm, it is one of the key findings of this study that all other persons, on the basis of their climactic experiencing, can be classified in one of three major groups.

a) *Mono-orgasmic* (mono, from the Greek, meaning one, single)
b) *Poly-orgasmic* (poly, from the Greek, meaning many)
c) *Hetero-orgasmic* (hetero, from the Greek, meaning various, different)

It should be noted that in *all* orgasmic individuals, regardless of the group, when an orgasm is triggered, stimulation of specific components of the sexual nervous system are involved and *a more general physiological response then takes place.* (Throughout this volume the terms "orgasm" and "climax" are used interchangeably.)

The Mono-Orgasmic Person

Mono-orgasmic means that a climax occurs at the peak of stimulation of <u>one</u> *of the components of* the sexual nervous system. In the male it is usually the penis; in the female it is usually either the clitoris or the vaginal/cervical complex. In short, the mono-orgasmic person has only one type of orgasm. The vast majority of people are mono-orgasmic. They appear to greatly enjoy the climactic experience and lead very satisfying sex lives.

The Poly-Orgasmic Person

Poly-orgasmic indicates that a climax can occur at the peak of stimulation *of more than one, or several, components of the sexual nervous system; yet all orgasms, regardless of the source of stimulation, feel essentially the same to the individual experiencing them.* A woman may, for example, be able to have an orgasm from clitoral or vaginal/cervical, or G-Spot stimulation to the peak, but each of these climaxes feels very much like the other. They all feel the same to the person.

A man, for example, may be able to have an orgasm from stimulation, to the peak, of the penis, or the prostate and the anus, but these climaxes will feel very much the same to him. If the poly-orgasmic person stimulates two sexual organs toward a climax, resulting in a fusion orgasm, this type of climax will feel very much like the other orgasms, but sometimes more intense. Most poly-orgasmic people, however, report the fusion climax as being more intense.

The Hetero-Orgasmic Person

Hetero-orgasmic means that a climax can occur at the peak of stimulation of more than one, or several, sexual nervous system components; *yet every orgasm has unique, differ-*

ent characteristics, associated with the point of stimulation, which differentiates it from all other orgasms. The hetero-orgasmic person is able to have orgasms from the excitation of a number of sexual nervous system components with each orgasm having unique or individual attributes associated with the source of stimulation. To the hetero-orgasmic woman, the orgasm triggered by stimulation of the clitoris feels *different* than one triggered by breast stimulation.

In the man, orgasm triggered by anal stimulation feels *different* from the one triggered by stimulation of the penis. If the hetero-orgasmic person stimulates two sexual nervous system components, at the same time, toward climax, his resultant *fusion orgasm* will have its own unique, distinct characteristics, different from all other orgasms. (Many, however, describe the fusion orgasm as being stronger than other climaxes.)

The vast majority of hetero-orgasmic persons are women. Reports by hetero-orgasmic people, describing their various types of orgasms, have been published in letter form in U.S. magazines for several decades. Some would like to believe that these letters result from the vivid imagination of paid hack writers. However, this is not the case. *Penthouse Forum* magazine, for example keeps reader letters on file.

Membership in the three core climactic groups is fluid

Membership in the three core classifications of the human climactic response is fluid in the sense that people may move from one category of orgasmic experiencing to another. This can take place as the result of self-development or training, or such change may take place spontaneously, on its own, so that a mono-orgasmic person may discover that he or she has become poly-orgasmic. Or a poly-orgasmic person may elect to become hetero-orgasmic through using various methods (See Chapters 10-11, pp. 183-213), or have this occur spontaneously.

Anyone who is able to differentiate between different types of orgasms—and thereby is hetero-orgasmic—has developed a capacity called *orgasm discrimination.* (How this capacity is acquired is not as yet known.) However, a hetero-orgasmic person, on suffering severe emotional or sexual trauma, may temporarily lose the ability to discriminate between climaxes and become poly-orgasmic, i.e. all orgasms feel the same. (Again, further study is needed, as only two such instances have come to my attention at the time of this writing.)

Mono and poly-orgasmic individuals, to whom all climaxes feel the same, appear to have a less rich and less varied range of climactic experiencing than those who are hetero-orgasmic. This in no way diminishes the enjoyment of their sex lives.

At this point, it is not yet known what factors such as attitudes and previous sexual experiences (or trauma) are involved in shaping the sexual functioning of a mono-orgasmic, poly-orgasmic, or hetero-orgasmic individual. It must again be repeated that members of one core climactic group are not superior or in any way "better" than members of another. Sexual experiencing is a personal preference similar to a preference for certain foods. Can it be said that the lover of French fries is in any way inferior to those who prefer their potatoes mashed, baked or served au gratin? No. *Chacun a son gout—* each to his or her own taste, when it comes to both sex and food. Finally, in the words of the pioneering sexologist David Scharch: "Some people enjoy their orifices more than others."

ORGASM FACTS

Different researchers present somewhat variant findings about the human climax. Whenever possible, this has been taken into consideration in the following compilation of interesting facts about the human orgasmic response.

- The woman's length of orgasm for a single climax has been clocked from ten seconds to one minute, with an average length of 19-28 seconds per climax. (Length of time appears to be increasing.)

- The average male orgasm is about 10-15 seconds in length. (Longer climaxes are being reported.)

- The writer's work with the Orgasm Spectrum Research Project has lead to the conclusion that as much as 75% of the human orgasm is an emotional/mental process.

- Both women and men can slow down the onset of their orgasms. There are also clear indications that the length, or duration, as well as the *intensity* of the climax can be increased.

- Once a man senses he has reached "the point of no return," or "ejaculatory inevitability," he cannot stop his orgasm from running its course.

- Some sexologists maintain that a woman can stop (or abort) an orgasm at any time. Others disagree and state that, after a certain point in the climactic process, a woman cannot bring an orgasm to a halt. It is very likely that this ability, or lack thereof, varies widely with the individual.

- For the average U. S. male, it takes from two to three and a half minutes from the time of insertion of the penis in the vagina to the point of ejaculation. This time is lengthening significantly.

- Only between 40% and 50% of American women regularly experience a climax during intercourse. The figures vary, but as high as 20% to 30% of U. S. women reportedly have *never* had an orgasm.

- Approximately fifteen to twenty percent of U. S. males (possibly more), experience difficulty controlling rapid ejaculation. Complete control over the onset of ejaculation appears to be relatively uncommon but is becoming more widespread.

- In a woman, vaginal contractions occur faster than she could *voluntarily* contract her muscles, namely at four-fifths of a second. The uterus and anal sphincter may also contract. Contractions may last from 3-5 minutes and up to 15 minutes.

- Male ejaculatory contractions occur at a rate of about one every 0.8 seconds, with the first 3-4 ejaculatory contractions the most powerful.

- Sexologists William Hartman and Marilyn Fithian, during their research, discovered 33 multi-orgasmic males (See Chapter 5, p. 85).

- The male refractory period (amount of time before a man can resume sexual/orgasmic activity) varies from minutes to hours.

- The majority of women need no refractory period and can have continuous sexual activity and orgasms. According to a recent report, some "hover" near peak ecstasy for an hour after the first orgasm. Others require seconds to minutes of rest before continuing.

RESISTANCE TO THE LIBERATED ORGASM AND OTHER NEW SEX FINDINGS

It is proverbial that anything new, whether it be a product or an idea, is going to be met with some resistance. The liberated orgasm is no exception. This is especially the case since deeply entrenched misinformation and established myths about sex have been repeated throughout human history.

Men can be expected to have the greatest resistance to the liberated orgasm. They have been told they can only have a penile orgasm for countless generations. Numerous men will be disturbed to learn that they have the potential to actualize five additional climactic options, plus the fusion and zone orgasms. Most men in the deepest sense of their being, while reading this information, know that it is correct and that they will not do anything about it. The social conditioning is too strong and operates to resist change.

26

The idea that the orgasm cannot be influenced and is solely an event dominated and reflexively triggered by the autonomous nervous system is a tale that continues to be spread (not only by "old wives," but also old husbands). *This misinformation provides ongoing conditioning for maintaining one of society's most deeply instilled fears—that our sexuality will get out of control and take us over.* Women are especially prone to this fear.

As part of our life experience, sex and especially the orgasm paradoxically fulfill dual needs. There is the need to be totally out of control during the climax versus the *conflicting* need to direct and shape the intensity and sequence of peak erotic rapture. (Most people appear not to be consciously aware of this second need.)

Why do we have such a strong need to be out of control while experiencing orgasm? The answer is that we are all so regimented, habituated and excessively controlled by our minds that the climactic experience has come to symbolize a type of "mindless freedom." It also blots out the ego and all reality, and feelings take over. This represents the essence and meaning of the orgasmic event for many. For some, orgasm is a moment in their lives when they feel truly free.

Most of us have also become deeply habituated to the orgasmic state of being called "chaotic ecstasy," (see also Chapter 7, p.127)—that short or long moment of highly intense pleasure which blots out all else. It is a pattern we do not wish to change, and the possibility of change evokes strong resistance. This is especially the case if the orgasm is associated with one's sense of freedom.

It is natural to cherish freedom and to resist discipline. However, the development of the orgasm requires the application of discipline. Also, we want everything right away and at once. The creative shaping of the orgasm (see Chapters 7, 9, 10, 11) takes time, effort and the investment of energy.

Involvement in orgasm shaping (Chapter 7, pp. 132-136), brings a new awareness of the many hidden dimensions of richness and new ecstatic feelings which can be found in the infinity of the orgasm. *A whole new universe for creative exploration is revealed—especially to those who like to be explorers on the path of life.*

Finally, what I have come to call the *camouflage effect of the human climax* creates its own strong resistance to orgasm development. The climax offers such an exquisite ecstatic experience (compared to other human pleasures), that it camouflages the fact that very significant increases in erotic pleasure—beyond the present level of climactic experiencing—remain an option. It is an option which the citizen of the 21st century will routinely explore.

It has been mentioned in the beginning of this section that people are resistant to new ideas—especially those in the area of human sexuality. A quite strong counter-thrust to such entrenched opposition also exists. People are curious about new sex findings and like to explore how they apply to their own sex lives.

We have called this phenomenon sexploration. There is a large and growing number of people in the U. S. and other parts of the world who enjoy experimenting with new and different erotic and sexual experiences. Sexploration foreshadows what is destined to be an even stronger movement.

It is called sexual self-development and is also already under way. A significant number of people are currently engaged in developing their erotic and sexual powers and capabilities (see Chapter 8, pp. 161-164). The actualizing of more of the vast human sexual potential can be expected to become a major movement in the first half of the 21st century.

THE INTERCOURSE AND ORGASM BELIEF SYSTEMS

An individual's beliefs about sex, intercourse and the climax are rarely examined, unless a problem arises which forces such a second look. Over the past two decades, behavioral scientists have increasingly found evidence that what we believe about an activity affects both our perception of the activity as well as the way we experience it. In short, *what we believe plays a major role in what we experience.* This is particularly true of sex. Our beliefs about sex clearly influence the nature of our sexual experiences.

Up until the mid-point of the twentieth century, most people in this country subscribed to traditional beliefs about sex and intercourse. The aims of coitus were generally defined as follows:

sex is for procreation
sex is for expressing love
sex is for fun and pleasure

Since the sixties, a growing number of people have become aware that there is more to sex than what is defined by traditional beliefs. Sex education and videos, plus the accessibility of sex books—including those describing the sex practices of other cultures—brought change.

In the mid-eighties, while beginning to work on the Orgasm Spectrum Research Project, I reviewed my own sex history in detail. I found that prior to my mid-thirties, my belief system about coitus strongly influenced what I experienced during sex. Following this discovery I found myself asking acquaintances and friends: "What, to you, is the meaning of intercourse?"

Intrigued by the responses, I decided to undertake a limited exploratory study. A review of the literature revealed that the subjective meanings of intercourse had received very little attention from researchers. No studies of the specific components of people's intercourse belief system appeared to have been conducted.

A Sexual Intercourse Belief System questionnaire was developed. It contained the question: "What, to you, is the meaning, or significance, of sexual intercourse? (What does the act of coitus, or sexual intercourse, mean to you?)" Interviews were held and 30 persons filled out an anonymous questionnaire which requested information about their gender, age and level of education. Of this number, 11 were men and 19 were women. Five had a high school education while 18 had graduated from college or had advanced degrees. The remainder had one or more years of college. Twenty of the respondents were 18 to 31 years of age, while the age of the remaining ten ranged from the late thirties to the sixties.

BASIC BELIEFS ABOUT INTERCOURSE

A considerable range of beliefs about intercourse were noted, as follows:

"Intercourse is my way of communicating physically, mentally, emotionally and spiritually with a man I care deeply for. With the sharing of pleasure, I give part of myself in a relationship. He too leaves part of himself in me—not only physically, but on every level of being." (Woman, age 31, college grad.)

* * *

"Sexual intercourse has two definitions for me. 1) Fucking—the act of having sex for the sake of achieving orgasm with little or no intimacy involved. 2) Making love — making love includes being sensual as well sexual, all at the same time. To me this represents the ultimate expression of oneself in its purest form. I prefer to make love as I find myself enjoying the vulnerability and genuineness of sharing my body with another. The actual act of 'intercourse' represents a level of trust that includes the willingness of myself to allow another to enter and come into my body. I love the feeling of being so vulnerable and alive." (Woman, age 24, college grad plus 2 years.)

* * *

"Sex to me means the ultimate or the epitome of human communication. (Man, age 52, 2 years college.)

* * *

"A way to be close . . . I think that it's natures way of encouraging intimacy. Although our society or whatever discourages it. Sex takes you outside of yourself. It means that you trust someone enough to let yourself go with them — love and trust."(Woman, age 27,college grad.)

* * *

"Intercourse can be a high or a low for me. I have found many times in my life it has been a low. This because of the manipulations, real or perceived, to get it — usually with me feeling I did not want to participate but could not say 'no' and maintain some stature in the woman's eyes or the eyes of 'society.' I have changed this through active decision. I also find it can be the best experience of life. When honesty and love are present with respect, sex, touching, intercourse can be a life giving and energizing experience. It was, when I was married and still in love, a great experience which energized and validated a lot of my self-appreciation. It would put me on a two-day high. Coitus is a vulnerability which can be either the best—if treated with integrity, or horrid—if treated as a tool. I prefer the best. Ahh, what joy. . ." (Man, age 26 years, college grad plus 2 years.)

* * *

"Intercourse is an opportunity to release pent up energy — a chance to connect with another human being in a close way—a chance to be playful—sex seems kind of mystical — spiritual, an elevated place." (Woman, age 45, college grad plus 1 year.)

* * *

"It means very little, usually just a means of relief. Very rarely is it personal." (Man, age 37, college grad.)

* * *

"Sexual intercourse accompanied by pleasurable feeling with a cherished person provides me with an op-

31

portunity to connect with a universal sense of self. It might be expressed as God's way of teaching me about the nature of the universe that is beyond everyday planetary experience. I tap into the vastness of the potentiality of spirit ('spirit' as that which is prior to form). It is also possible to experience a oneness with all. It is a cosmic gift. I know who I am." (Woman, age 45, college grad +6 years.)

* * *

"Sexual intercourse is the physical playground of life which in turn is a book of artistic wonders. Within the wonders—satisfaction and silence." (Man, age 23, 1 year of college.)

* * *

"It is an intimate act and is best experienced (for me) as an expression of love and desire for my partner which flourished in a trusting, close relationship." (Woman, age 40, 3 years of college.)

* * *

"The primary purposes of the sexual union is a) to grow in sensitivity, empathy, compassion and self-understanding and to actively develop the capacity to experience pleasure; b) to develop more love and caring for self, other human beings and the Ground of Being. We are never more open to another person (and our own growth) than before, during or after sex. Sex is a means of a mutual, energy exchange on many deep levels. It provides an option for mutual evolution if that is the intent and purpose. The sexual connection is a form of revitalization—a restoration of hope and a rekindling of the embers of love." (Man, age 59, college grad + 4 years.)

* * *

"I like to shoot off. It's a great exercise and tension release. I just like to fuck." (Man, age 26, high school grad.)

*****

"Intercourse may serve to strengthen the participants' emotional bond with each other, and I believe that this is one of its most positive, constructive functions. Sexual intercourse can be an eloquent expression of feelings that may appear to be beyond the reach of verbalization." (Woman, age 22, college grad.)

*****

Results of The Intercourse Belief System Study

This relatively youthful group, with an above-average educational background, yielded interesting findings. Eight dominant themes emerged from an analysis of the data. The following themes appear to spell out the broad range of contemporary meanings of sexual intercourse for members of this—and possibly other—Western societies. (The themes are not listed in any particular order.)

a. Hygienic Sex—sex as a tension release; for relaxation,sex for energy; "sex is therapeutic," or improves health.

b. Recreational sex—sport sex; sex for fun, pleasure, enjoyment.

c. Sex for intimacy, bonding, closeness, to express trust; for sharing of self; as a form of intimate communication.

d. Sex as an expression of marital union, for procreation.

e. Sex for love and romance; to express affection, love, caring.

f. The sexual union as an opportunity for personal evo-

lution, personal growth, sexual self-knowledge or increased self-understanding.

g. Sex to deepen the love of self and humanity.

h. Intercourse as a path of spiritual, transcendental or
mystical experiencing.

It was an important finding of this study that the *majority of participants used a combination of the above themes to
describe the meaning of coitus.* Ascribing only one meaning to
intercourse was uncommon.

EFFECTS OF THE INTERCOURSE
AND ORGASM BELIEF SYSTEMS

This limited study yielded some findings which are of
particular value to those interested in the possible restructuring of their sexual belief system. The effects of the belief
system on the individual experience of the sex act varied
widely. There are strong indications that for many, the meanings associated with intercourse and orgasm play a significant role in what transpires during and to some extent, after,
the sexual union. Interviews yielded a number of revealing
conclusions:

• Their sexual belief system for many, if not most
people functions to severely restrict their experience
of sexual pleasure.

• In some instances the intercourse belief system
seems to influence the availability of sex energy, or
the presence and absence of desire.

• The intensity of the orgasmic experience also may
be affected by the belief system.

• Individuals—and especially men—who perceive intercourse as primarily a means of tension release, or physical/mental hygiene, appear to have a tendency to fall asleep immediately following intercourse. Significantly, a number of men in this sub-group used the term "having my ashes hauled," when referring to intercourse. For some, their climax seems to be quite short and lacking in intensity.

• Some people have, what can be called "an impoverished intercourse belief system." On the extreme scale of the impoverished systems are those beliefs which can undermine the individual's self-image and restrict sexual enjoyment. Examples of these include:

"Sex is unclean, dirty business and you do it only to have children." (woman)

"Fucking is the animal part of man. You act out the animal in you." (man)

"Fucking in all its forms is sinful and the devil's work." (man)

"You stick it in. You like it. You come. You pull it out. That's it!" (man)

"You screw because your parents tell you not to and it feels good." (woman)

The interviews yielded another persistent response. Men—especially those who largely perceived coitus as a means of relaxation, or tension release—reported three types of post-orgasmic patterns. After climaxing, they either very quickly fell asleep for the rest of the night, had a short nap, or entered a dream-like, deeply quiet state for a period of time with no talking.

Religious convictions appear to influence the intercourse belief system—at least to the extent of determining some aspects of a person's sexual behavior.

Over the past three decades, sexologists have done considerable research to determine the influence of religious beliefs on the sex life. Many of these studies clearly indicate that persons with a strong religious interest were less sexually active than others, and that "conventional religiosity has a significant inhibiting effect upon sexual behavior for attached and unattached men as well as women."(1)

The influence of religion on sex appears to be diminishing. This trend will very likely gather momentum, especially after the first quarter of the new century. Significantly, the Janus Report of Sexual Behavior found that 31% of the "very religious," of their participants, have had an extra-marital affair at least once. (2)

The intercourse belief system of young people differs from that of the older generations. "Making it" is not as loaded with as much guilt, shame and ambivalence. The sex act is more accepted. It may also be more objectified and treated as an act not associated with feelings of love, caring and affection. ("You eat, drink and sleep and you fuck—it's not that big a deal.") Further research is needed.

An analysis of contemporary beliefs about intercourse would be incomplete without a discussion of the hidden aspects of the system. Regardless of how people describe what coitus means to them, there are some largely unconscious emotional components to their beliefs, of which they may not be totally aware.

Prominent among *the hidden aspects of the intercourse belief system* are strong feelings of disgust, shame and guilt about the physiological aspects of sex. Also included are feelings which are the result of early, negative parental conditioning about sex which renders it essentially a taboo activity. (For example, parents labeling sex as "dirty," sinful, lustful, bad, or an "animal part" of the human being.) Some also fear the loss of control during coitus and the climax. The complex emotions which result from strong negative incidents associated with sex, i.e. trauma, also plays an important role.

This combination of (sometimes) accessible (but more often) hidden forces can exert a marked influence on the experience of intercourse. If restructuring of the belief system is to be considered, a hard look needs to be taken at these hidden aspects of the system. In some instances, sex counseling may be required to bring about fundamental change.

Analysis and restructuring of the intercourse belief system and the orgasmic belief system is a timely undertaking. Timely, because it is in tune with what is currently happening (about sex) in this country. In the last few years, a number of well-known authors have observed *that a redefinition of sex and the meaning of sex is underway.*

Couples who have shared their intercourse belief system with their partner report two interesting results. First, talking about their beliefs is not too difficult and is helpful in fostering communication about sex. Most important, sharing about the meanings of intercourse deepens feelings of closeness and intimacy.

Recent research has revealed that emotional and mental elements play an important role in the experience of the orgasm. As previously mentioned, our beliefs about intercourse can influence the nature of the climax as well as what happens post-coitally. *Gains in sex energy are observed when change—or a restructuring of the intercourse belief system takes place.* One woman commented: "About two weeks after writing my improved ideas about intercourse, I noticed something. I was having more fun with sex and wanted it more."

Restructuring of the intercourse belief system can be initiated by a simple exercise. Write out the heading: "What, to you, is the meaning, or significance, of sexual intercourse?" Now answer this question, in writing, as fully as you can. Let a few days elapse and review what you have written. Finally, use your will power to make changes and rewrite what you have written, if necessary. During this process, sharing what you have written with someone close to you is helpful.

There is every indication that to a very considerable *extent the contemporary heterosexual male especially is prisoner of his orgasm belief system.* As previously mentioned, he has been conditioned to believe that he is capable of only the penile climax. For most, this significantly reduces interest in exploring other orgasm options.

Restricting the male to the penile orgasm reinforces

the macho image. Judging by the reactions of some sexologist colleagues to the Man's Basic Six orgasms, the belief that the male can have only a penile orgasm appears to be sacrosanct. Somehow the idea of the man being capable of having more than one type of orgasm seems to spoil the "purity" of the male image. One can almost hear the comment: "Real men have only penile orgasms." Most men, in the deepest sense of their being, on reading that they have other orgasm options know that this is correct. They also know they will not do much about it. The social conditioning is too strong.

The impact of the belief system on the sexual experience, for some, may be hard to detect. To the individual immersed in his or her system, regardless of its content, sex is still the greatest pleasure in life. There is no basis for comparison until a change in the system is set in motion and takes place. The resulting changes may be dramatic. On the other hand change may be subtle, since alterations in ecstatic pleasure levels may take time to develop.

In my sexual enrichment classes, the experience of exploring the intercourse belief system was described by participants as "very revealing." Quite often, class members found that, as a result of using a simple written exercise about the belief system, they discovered something new about themselves or their relationship.

Early in the twentieth century, the American psychologist William James concluded that we tend to live too far within self-imposed limits. This is especially true about our sexuality which, in turn, is largely governed by our sexual belief system.

It must be repeated that the culture, or society, very largely determines the individual's belief system about sex. This, in turn, strongly influences the sex attitudes—what a person thinks about sex as well as the intensity and other qualities of his or her sexual experiencing on the feeling level. The most comprehensive and prestigious study of sexual attitudes and beliefs was published in the November 1998 *Journal of Sex Research.* The following summarizes the findings about America's tremendous ambivalence about human sexuality:

"The United States is distinctive—markedly more conservative than most European nations in its sexual attitudes. *In fact, American attitudes toward* nonmarital sex
class it with Ireland, Northern Ireland and Poland—three
nations associated with conservative Catholic populations.
Other nominally Catholic countries (e.g., Italy) do not fall
into this cluster, so the common denominator of the
Sexual Conservatives is not religion per se. An analysis
of ISSP data on church attendance, however, does show
that the countries grouped as Sexual Conservatives are
those where people report attending church frequently."
(3) Emphasis added.

The citizens of tomorrow will be aware of all these facts,
thus empowering themselves to liberate and actualize more of
their sexual potential. The power of sex becomes a transfor-
mational force.

On completing reading of this book, the reader will be
in possession of considerable new information about sex and
the orgasm. The new knowledge that the orgasm can be
formed, developed or shaped, can have a strong impact on the
sexual belief system. This may be a particularly auspicious
time to undertake a restructuring of this system.

Notes

1. Alan R. Sack, James F. Keller, and Denise Hinkle, "Pre-marital Sexual" Intercourse: A Test of the Effect of Peer Group, Religiosity and Sexual Guilt," *Journal of Sex Research*, 2 (1984): 172.

2. Samuel S. Janus and Cynthia L. Janus, *The Janus Report on Sexual Behavior*, (John Wiley and Sons, 1993): 165.

3. Eric D. Widmer, Judith Treas and Robert Newcomb, "Attitudes Toward Nonmarital Sex in 24 Countries," *The Journal of Sex Research*, 4 (1998):356.

CHAPTER 3

THE WOMAN'S BASIC SEVEN
Part I

Every woman is potentially capable of having *seven basic types of orgasms.* In addition to the basic seven, women are capable of combinations of the basic seven, called the *fusion* orgasm and the *zone* orgasm (described in Chapter 6, pp. 107-110). The woman's basic seven will be discussed in detail in this and the next chapter.

It will be recalled that in the course of the Orgasm Spectrum Research Project, a total of 335 participants filled out a copy of the Orgasmic Range Survey . This primary group consisted of 205 women and 130 men. Findings from this relatively youthful group, with an above-average educational background, are included in this and the next two chapters.

These *basic seven* climaxes available to women have unique and distinct characteristics for the hetero-orgasmic person. This basic spectrum of the female climax includes: 1) the clitoral orgasm, 2) the vaginal/cervical orgasm, 3) the breast orgasm, 4) the mouth orgasm, 5) the G-spot orgasm, 6) the anal orgasm, and 7) the mental orgasm. Before taking a closer look at the *basic seven,* some additional important facts known about female orgasms will be reviewed. (In this and all subsequent chapters, the terms "orgasm" and "climax" are used interchangeably.)

ORGASMS, MULTIPLE ORGASMS
AND ORGASM VARIANTS

Women were not believed capable of experiencing orgasm until some time *after* the turn of the twentieth century. Concurring in this mistaken belief were well-known medical

41

authorities. Middle-class women were instructed to do their "marital or wifely duties" and were told that "decent" and "proper" women derived no pleasure from sex. Reproductive sex for the creation of children was the rule. Sex was the man's prerogative and he had sex with a woman for his own enjoyment. While this cluster of cultural/theological biases still persists in numerous fundamental faiths and various nations, it is now generally accepted that both genders are capable of enjoying and experiencing sex and the orgasm.

Not only are women capable of being orgasmic, many women are also capable of having *multiple orgasms*, i.e. several climaxes in quick succession. Some have them whenever they wish, and without difficulty. Others have them only under certain circumstances—being in the right mood, being with the right partner, being in the optimal position for coitus, being in the right environment, etc. While the vast majority of women are *potentially* capable of multiple orgasms, many choose not to, do not, or cannot, for various reasons, actualize this potential.

Women who do have multiple orgasms may experience only vaginal and anal contractions, or they may experience a more major climax involving contractions of various parts of the body which may last for a minute or longer. They may also have a series of minor orgasms which are experienced as less intense and may result in several minor, or to them non-observable muscular contractions. Some climaxes may also succeed each other quite swiftly, with very brief delay between orgasms. They are then known as a *continuous* orgasm, or as *sequential* orgasms. Multiple orgasms can include a mix of climaxes with varying intensities. Little is as yet known about the capacity for multiple orgasms vis-a-vis most of the Basic Seven.

Most, but not all women, during their orgasms, experience three to fifteen muscular contractions which occur less than one second apart. Two major types of vaginal contractions occur during the female orgasm. One contraction involves the outer third of the vaginal muscles. A deeper type of contraction involves the muscles of the uterus and the deep musculature of the pelvis and anus. While some women are unaware that these contractions take place, they do exist and can be measured.

The *whole body orgasm* must also be mentioned. It is reported to involve the whole body or numerous body parts, and was mentioned by a number of women participants throughout the duration of this study. The whole body orgasm can take place in a variety of contexts. During the eighties, four women who were disciples of the mystic guru Bhagwan Shree Rajneesh talked to me about their whole body orgasms. They reported having had this type of climax while dancing before the guru in Poona, India.

On subsequently attending a gathering of his disciples in the U. S., I found another half dozen women who were aware of this phenomenon. They reported that friends had told them of having experienced this particular type of climax. This type of *whole body orgasm* appears to represent a melding of spiritual and sexual ecstasy.

In the spring of 1996, I met a successful young businessman who had also been to Poona as an attendant to Bhagwan. He was aware that I was doing research on the human climax and volunteered that he had experienced a "dancing orgasm." It was very similar to those described by the women. This seems to indicate that men are also capable of the type of whole body orgasm which takes place in a spiritual context. More research about the *whole body orgasm* is needed.

As previously noted, there is some dispute about a woman's capacity to abort, or stop, the orgasm once it is in mid-course or beyond. My observation has been that some women can and some cannot stop their orgasms. There are numerous women who can only climax through masturbation. Sexologist Joseph LoPiccolo makes a telling point when discussing those women who are orgasmic during masturbation but not with their partners. He states that in many cases, the old maxim "There are no frigid women, only clumsy men" is true if the woman is normally responsive but the male is an inept lover. He adds: "The principle of mutual responsibility, however, points out that such a woman has failed to *train* her husband to be an effective lover *for her*." (1)

LoPiccolo suggests that a revision of the old maxim be made so that it will read: "There are both frigid women and clumsy men, and they are usually married to each other." By the same token, a number of sexologists, Helen Singer Kaplan among others, believe that for a sizable group of women, sexual responsiveness *without* orgasm may be normal. I disagree—this is not a "normal" phenomenon.

Although fairly rare, some women suffer from a condition known as "premature orgasm." Such orgasms occur shortly after intromission of the penis into the vagina and usually are not very intense. Anxiety, lack of self-confidence or sexual self-esteem are some of the factors which may contribute to this condition, which is not without its similarities to premature ejaculation in a man.

The physician and sexologist Avodah Offit refers to what she calls "the incomplete orgasm." (2) Such an orgasm may begin, then stop and fade away before total release is achieved. Finally there, is "orgasmic anesthesia," a state characterized by some signs of an orgasm (such as vaginal contractions), but without pleasurable or erotic sensations. How many women suffer from these latter orgasmic variants is unknown.

While conducting interviews for this study, a number of sexually sophisticated women mentioned that if they had several orgasms during an encounter with a partner, these climaxes successively increased in strength. I would agree with sexologist Mary Jane Sherfey's conclusion that numerous women fail to be satisfied by one strong orgasm. (3) As women's fear of their own sexuality decreases, it can be expected that a growing number of women will experience a substantial increase in the intensity of each successive climax. I call this the *accelerated orgasmic intensity process*. It appears to be exclusively restricted to the female of the species.

Some women need several orgasms to obtain a feeling of satisfaction, relaxation and lovingness, or to achieve an orgasm with deep contractions. Others need a specific series of climaxes to achieve an optimal feeling of fulfillment. For example, one woman reported that "to really feel fulfilled," she would like a clitoral, a vaginal and an anal orgasm in the course of an evening with her lover.

1. THE CLITORAL ORGASM

The clitoral orgasm occurs at the peak of clitoral stimulation; it appears to *begin in the clitoris and may expand from there.* For a period of almost two decades, this type of orgasm, due to the information provided by sexologists Masters and Johnson, was widely believed to be the *only* orgasm of which women were capable. Only a few years ago, this misleading notion began to be recognized for what it is—a conspicuous misconception.

In the light of recent history, the contributions made by Masters and Johnson have begun to emerge in a clearer perspective. They were the first to monitor and film internal physiological processes which took place during a woman's sexual arousal and orgasm. Valuable contributions were made to our understanding of this process.

At the same time, Masters and Johnson became the major proponents of a doctrine subsequently called *clitorocentrism* by sexologists. This is the erroneous belief that a woman's capacity to experience orgasm is basically and primarily dependent on her clitoris. Masters and Johnson strongly promoted this myth for about two decades. The effects of this false information cannot be overestimated. Due to the pervasive U. S. cultural clitorocentral conditioning, the clitoris—for many, if not most—women continues to be the major—if not only—source of their climax.

In 1992, Masters And Johnson, with co-author Robert Kolodny, published their volume *Heterosexuality.* They again asserted their doctrine of clitorocentrism in this publication. It is of interest, however, that the authors do refer to a woman's capacity to have a number of additional, different types of orgasms. They buried the reference to this fact in the back of this book, in their notes for Chapter Three.

"Even when a woman is orgasmic from *fantasy alone,* with no physical stimulation whatever, she is likely to feel the sensation start in her clitoris. Similarly, orgasms that occur during activities like *anal intercourse* or *breast stimulation,* where there is no genital touching at all, still have

45

the build-up of the orgasmic platform and seem to have orgasm triggered with a sensation that is first felt in the clitoris. (4) Emphasis added.

It is my observation that neither the mental orgasm, nor the breast or anal orgasms, are routinely "first felt in the clitoris" by the woman. Most women interviewed for this study mentioned the breasts or anus as the starting point for these climaxes. Evidently women vary in their identification of the orgasmic starting points. (For more re Masters and Johnson's research, see p. 67 in the next chapter.)

What is the clitoris and its location?
The clitoris is located below the mons veneris on the anterior portion of the vulva. The inner vaginal lips (labia minora) partially hide it from view. Where the inner lips meet, small folds of skin form the frenulum which looks like an inverted V. The inner vaginal lips are attached to the underside of the clitoris and thus play an important role in the network of nerves which transmit sexual stimulation.

The junction of the inner vaginal lips forms the clitoral hood. This tiny hood covers the clitoris in much the same manner as a foreskin covers a penis. If the hood is pulled back, the glans or tip of the clitoris—roughly the size of a pencil eraser—is exposed. The tip of the clitoris is richly supplied with nerves. Immediately after orgasm it may retract, since it can become highly sensitive to further stimulation, to the point of being painful.

The shaft of the clitoris is hidden from view but can be felt. It is located immediately above the hood, and can be felt moving beneath the touch when its erectile tissue is aroused and lubricated. The shaft carries powerful sexual pleasure impulses deep into the pelvic region. In women, the internal sexual nervous system involves the clitoral shaft plus adjacent areas, as well as the system of nerves within the deeper pelvic structure.

How important is the clitoris?
For most women, *indirect* stimulation of the clitoris plays a major role in the clitoral orgasm. According to Mas-

ters and Johnson, the vaginal inward thrusting of the penis exerts traction on both the inner vaginal lips and clitoral hood, tending to exert a downward pull on the clitoris. On the withdrawal stroke of the penis, lips and hood are released, returning the clitoris to its original position. The in-and-out thrusting of the penis thus induces a rhythmic motion to the glans and clitoral shaft—an indirect form of stimulation.

There is currently considerable disagreement among sexologists about the *indirect mechanism of clitoral stimulation* during intercourse, as proposed by Masters and Johnson. Author Shere Hite, for example, who denies the existence of any vaginal trigger points, dismissed this indirect mechanism as implausible. She is joined in this view by the respected French sexologist G. Zwang, who reached a similar conclusion. Sexologists Ladas, Whipple and Perry make the following illuminating remarks about the clitoris:

"Even in its traditional, limited formulation, the clitoris is more complicated than most researchers have acknowledged. A glance at any standard anatomy text reveals that, in addition to the primary nerve connections that the tip or glans of the clitoris has with the pudendal nerve, the shaft and its attachments are believed to be connected to the pelvic nerve deeper inside the body. This fact, often overlooked by sex researchers, *has important implications and helps* to explain the tremendous variety of response patterns that different *women enjoy.*" (5) Emphasis added.

The female superior, or woman-on-top position of intercourse, appears to allow for the most intensive stimulation of the clitoris. There is usually no contact between penis and clitoris in this position, but a very firm contact between the man's pubic region with the clitoral area takes place. Many women exhibit muscular tension (myotomia) as their sexual tension mounts. This tension is manifest in highly individualistic movements. The legs or body may vibrate, the pelvic area may move up and down and the back may arch in pleasure. *Some women misinterpret the increasing sexual tension as a sign of anxiety rather than recognizing it as an indication of mounting sexual excitement.*

The clitoral and other types of stimulation produces what Masters and Johnson call the "ballooning" or "tent effect," wherein there is a ballooning of the vagina along with a lifting of the uterus. A space is created in the vagina and the vaginal opening tightens as the orgasmic platform is formed. At the time of orgasm, there is a general contraction of the pelvic muscles as well as those of the vaginal and anal sphincters. Contraction of the uterus also takes place in many women.

What are the effects of clitoral circumcision?

The glans or head of the clitoris and the shaft are so well supplied with nerves that even the removal of the head (clitoridectomy) does not deprive most women of a clitoral orgasm, although their peak pleasure level may decline. Clitoridectomy was practiced in the U.S. at the turn of the century. It is still practiced by certain African tribes and some middle class families in Eastern countries. (In 1996, Egypt prohibited this practice by law.) The declared purpose of this operation—which in more enlightened countries is viewed as barbaric—is to control masturbation and dampen the female sex drive.

Sexologist Hanny Lightfoot-Klein offers the following observation about female circumcision:

"In a study conducted over a 5-year period, the author interviewed over 300 Sudanese women and 100 Sudanese men on the sexual experience of circumcised and infibulated women. Sudanese circumcision involves excision of the clitoris, the labia minora and the inner layers of the labia majora, and fusion or infibulation of the bilateral wound. The findings of this study indicate that sexual desire, pleasure and orgasm are experienced by the majority of women who have been subjected to this extreme sexual mutilation, in spite of their also being culturally bound to hide these experiences. *These findings* also seriously question the importance of the clitoris as an organ that must be stimulated in order to produce female orgasm, *as is often maintained in Western literature.* (6) Emphasis added.

Psychological factors associated with the clitoral orgasm

For some women, the clitoral climax is closely linked to its historical significance vis-a-vis the women's movement of the mid-sixties and seventies. At that time, the clitoris acquired important symbolic attributes which added another dimension of meaning to the climax. The clitoral orgasm was associated with the declaration of a woman's rights to her own body, and to her own way of sexual fulfillment—with or without a man. She had become sexually independent and no longer has to rely on a penis for sexual satisfaction.

The clitoris is anatomically homologous to the penis, and the strength of its response to stimulation is certainly as powerful as that of the male organ. The clitoris has been the center of attention for so long that women are beginning to ask: "is that all there is?" Yet the power and clarity of the clitoral orgasm cannot be denied.

The clitoris as the sole source of orgasm may be favored by women who fear being too passive or too submissive. For some women, it may represent a way of guarding against closeness or intimacy. The clitoral climax may also symbolize a contact of externals and a closure to the interior pleasures of the vaginal/cervical orgasm. The intensity and sharp quality of the clitoral climax conveys a sense of vitality and energy, a feeling of being in control. On a deeper level, the orgasm can also become a means of conquest, or a form of dominating or controlling. It is also a way of being in charge.

The clitoris is the most readily available organ for sensual excitation during childhood and pubescence. Studies have shown that this type of self-arousal and climax is a widespread practice, unless strongly or traumatically discouraged by parents. Most girls appear to learn about their sexual functioning from their clitoris. This early learning readily establishes habitual modes of satisfaction. Many women, true to their early sex life patterns, *refrain from carrying their own sexual explorations much beyond the clitoris.* Thus, it can easily become the primary or exclusive center of sexual satisfaction.

Each woman has her individual way to achieve her own version of the best possible clitoral climax. She can teach her partner how to induce such a climax through a combination of touch, demonstration and verbal instructions. Unfortunately, many women are too shy to do so and many men resent such instructions which they feel impinge on their "machismo." It is possible, however, for a woman to teach a man how to play with her clitoris by asking him to observe her as she masturbates.

How does a clitoral orgasm feel

A large number of women refer to their clitoral orgasms as "very intense but not as deep as some others." Nevertheless, many women find them extremely satisfying as their sole mode of climaxing. Still others prefer to begin sexual relations with a series of clitoral orgasms, then proceed to other forms of stimulation. Descriptions of clitoral orgasms show wide variations:

"The thrill starts there (clitoris) and takes over my whole body. Waves of outrageously intense pleasure wash over me. I lose myself."

"Clitoral orgasm begins with very mild tingly nerve sensations. Before intensity starts, extreme sensitivity is apparent. It's extremely intense. I reach oblivion quickly."

"I once counted eleven different types of clitoral orgasms in one masturbatory session. Some were focused and intense. Others brought a sensation of heat. Others involved vibrations or spasming and subsequent retraction of the clitoris."

Because the clitoral orgasm can be felt again and again in a short period of time, with new peaks of ecstasy, it delivers a most valuable psychological bounty. This is the bounty of hope—the feeling that good things can, and will, happen again in the future. In this sense, mastery of the clitoral orgasm is one way to build sexual confidence.

Study Findings
Of all women (205) from the Primary Group participating in this research, 88% (182) reported having clitoral orgasms.

2. THE VAGINAL/CERVICAL ORGASM

The vaginal/cervical orgasm involves the barrel of the vagina as well as the cervix—the mouth of the uterus—and may involve the uterus itself. The orgasm takes place at the peak of stimulation of the vagina and cervix, which may begin in the vagina and/or cervix and may expand from there. Sexologists Whipple and Perry, et al, call this process the "A-frame effect." With vaginal stimulation, the uterus does not elevate and the vagina remains snug. The vaginal opening becomes more lax and with the approach of orgasm there is a bearing down effect, as if an object is being ejected from the vagina. Contractions of the pelvic muscles and uterus, as well as the anus may occur. At the point of orgasm, it sometimes happens that the penis (or any object being used for stimulation) is pushed out by the strength of the contractions.

How does this compare with the clitoral orgasm?
The vaginal orgasm, which is normal, natural and readily available, received mixed reviews in the sexological press of yesteryear. In the past, a number of anatomical and medical studies erroneously concluded that the vaginal walls showed no evidence of sexual nerve endings. For example, in a study completed in 1979 (prior to the rediscovery of the G-spot), the Israeli physician Zwi Hoch concluded that:

"The vagina *in most of its parts*, proves to be rather poorly endowed with 'sexual nerve ending.' Its posterior wall is *practically lacking* in any erotic feelings, and so are, *in most instances*, both lateral vaginal walls. Very few women reported some *slight* erotic sensations on stimulation of the so-called 'centers of sexual sensory perception at 4 o'clock and 8 o'clock described by Kegel." (7) Emphasis added.

It will be noted that Zwi Hoch qualified his observations, leaving the door open to the presence, in the vagina, of some sexual nerve endings.

The physician Heli Alzate, a professor of sexology in Colombia, noted in research published in 1985 that: "From recent empirical studies, it can be concluded that most *(and probably all) women possess vaginal zones whose tactile stimulation can lead to orgasm."* (8) My own observations coincide with those of Professor Alzate and other recent researchers. There is evidence that the *sensitivity of the vaginal barrel varies with the person.* The location of sensitive spots also varies. It is indisputable that many women *are* vaginally sensitive and can achieve a vaginal/cervical climax.

How does this orgasm come about?

One of the best-known elements that contribute to the vaginal/cervical orgasm is the in and out motion of the penis and the consequent rhythmic "pounding" which identifies the pelvic thrusting that takes place during intercourse. There is pressure from the expansion of the vagina while strong rhythmic vibrations are generated by the movement of the two bodies during the conjunction of sexual organs. These vibrations induce pleasure in the <u>cervix</u> and <u>uterus</u> as well as in the vagina. It is also evident that, for many women, *the G-Spot is involved in the vaginal-cervical orgasm.* (The G-Spot is discussed in the next chapter, p. 66.)

In 1980, French physician Gilbert Tordjman noted that " . . . next to the uterine cervix and vaginal cul de sac, there is a rich plexus of sensory nerve endings." (9) It is not surprising, therefore, that some women can feel the man ejaculating his semen into the cervical opening. Uterine contractions during orgasm have long been noted by sexologists—some women are aware of these and find them pleasurable.

On introduction of the penis (or equivalent), numer-

ous women are able to identify pleasurable feelings of distention or fullness of the vagina. If the penis is thick or large in
circumference, a small number of women experience orgasm
from the sensations accompanying the *introduction of the penis alone.* Other women report increased pleasure from the
distention of the vaginal walls by a thick penis, while a minority describe this distention as ranging from uncomfortable to
painful, although these sensations may gradually fade.

*The vaginal/cervical orgasm also involves the cervix or
mouth of the uterus.* Therefore, the slow introduction of an
exceptionally *lengthy* penis may trigger an orgasm if the head
of the male organ touches the cervix. (For some, this climax
is largely triggered by initial pressure on—and stimulation of—
the cervical area, without any "pumping" of the penis.) There
are also reports of the mouth of the cervix actually widening
to admit the head of the penis. Sometimes suction appears to
be generated by uterine contractions as the uterus takes in
the semen. I experienced this suction early in my sexual history.

When married to my first wife, we decided, after the
birth of our first daughter, that she was so cute and loving
that we wanted another baby. Following that decision, we
had intercourse during the most auspicious period for conception. We climaxed simultaneously. At this point, and for
the first and only time in my life, I felt dual sensations in addition to the orgasm—the penis head entering the mouth of
the cervix and a distinct sucking sensation as my semen was
drawn into my wife's uterus. My wife was certain she had
conceived and told me it would be a boy. (It was.)

Many women report that the cervix is especially sensitive to stimulation. This sensitivity also extends to the uterus
which is affected by the rhythmic penile thrusting during intercourse. The impressive number of reports by women not-
ing both painful (related to menstruation) and pleasurable (related to breast feeding as well as intercourse) sensations, at-
test to the sensitivity of this female organ. That the uterus
plays an important role in the woman's sexual nervous system cannot be denied.

Does a vaginal/cervical orgasm always require a man?

All manner of sex toys including dildos and insertable vibrators may make the presence of a penis all but irrelevant to some women. In fact, over many centuries, tens of thousands of Asian women have achieved orgasm through the stimulation of the vagina and cervix by the use of a pair of ben-wa balls. The early version of the ben-wa (known in France as *pommes d'amour*) consisted of two small spheres of ivory, bone or metal. One of these was a hollow ball. The other (called the male) was also hollow but contained mercury or an insert made of heavy metal. The hollow sphere was fitted against the cervix. The male ball was then placed in touch with it. Any movement of the woman's hips could thus induce vibrations which were transmitted to the cervix and uterus. The orgasms induced by this sex toy were said to be especially intense. (The modern version consists of one or two ovoid plastic spheres, one containing a small electric vibrator.)

The widespread use of sex toys which stimulate the vagina, cervix and G-Spot, are further proof that these organs are important components of a woman's sexual nervous system. We must conclude, then, that reports which seek to denigrate the vagina and cervix as a source of erotic sensitivity are totally erroneous and fall into the category of misinformation.

How does a vaginal/cervical orgasm feel?

"It begins with an itch in my vagina. It gets stronger until there is an explosion which spreads throughout my body. I can feel the vagina and uterus contracting. I am no longer here—on another planet."

"I was held on a plateau for a long period of time before final orgasm. It was totally spastic—longer lasting. It was more of a repeatable thing. I could reach several in short order."

"It felt like a contained pressure growing, exploding through a muscular physical barrier or gateway, then a spasm expanding to my belly and thighs.

A rush of energy down my legs and my toes, at the same time up my abdomen into my chest though my throat and out my head with waves of pulsings in my arm muscles, hands and fingers."

Psychological factors associated with the Vaginal/cervical orgasm

Some women are still influenced by Freud's antiquated preference for the vaginal orgasm as the more "mature" one. For them and for others, this type of orgasm may be experienced as both more fulfilling and as a form of reassurance. The insertion of the penis into the vagina can have a number of meanings on a deeper symbolic level. It can mean the ultimate acceptance and "taking in," or containing within one's self, of a loved one. Incorporation of the penis into the vagina can also be seen as a way of attaining greater emotional wholeness or completion. ("When you are inside me, I feel whole.") In addition, it can represent an essential melding, completion, or unification of two beings into one, however temporary.

For others, the emotional significance of the penis entering the vagina may be one of being conquered, or overcome, or dominated by a man. It may signal the onset of feelings of passivity. The act can also signify the domination, subduing or conquest of the male by (ultimately) causing his once-erect, proud penis to become limp and flaccid. "Taking the starch out of him" is the symbolic, folksy comment often heard in this regard.)

More rarely does the orgasm itself signal the triumphant conclusion of the "battle of the sexes," or symbolize a joust of aggression, hostility or rape. Conversely, the vaginal/cervical climax can be seen as the ultimate act of vulnerability, openness and giving of the self to a lover—in complete honesty and without masks. Avodah Offit makes this observation about the symbolism of vaginal intercourse:

"For a woman to allow herself to be deeply penetrated, filled by and aware of a man's penis in a totally receptive sense, while at the same time grasping it, closing around it, moving it with all the intensity of her body and spirit, in a totally active sense, seems to me to be a reflection of her capacity to enjoy the most intimate sexual union." (10)

There is every indication that women will increasingly discover and become more aware of their capacity to experience the vaginal-cervical orgasm. A new surge of interest in this type of orgasm will be a hallmark of the 21st century.

Study Findings
Of all women (205) from the Primary Group participating in this research, 60% (122) reported having vaginal-cervical orgasms.

3. THE BREAST ORGASM

The breast orgasm happens at the peak of stimulation of the breasts, may begin with the breasts and may expand from there. Many women become acquainted with this climax early in their sex life history. It continues to enjoy considerable popularity.

The breasts and nipples are of singular importance in the total sexual nervous system of a woman. The nipples are directly connected to the feminine genital nervous system. Many, if not most, women feel a direct connection with the genitals when the nipples are stimulated. ("When he plays with my nipples a current goes straight to my pussy and I get wet at once.")

Depending on the type of climax, different components of the sexual nervous system play a different (or more dominant) role. During the breast orgasm, many women note uterine contractions not present during the clitoral climax. Other women become generally excited from nipple stimulation *but do not feel a direct connection to the genitals.* ("I love attention to my nipples and breasts—I get excited all over and goose bumps run down my back. It feels like a lot of energy is concentrated in my nipples and breasts.")

56

When mothers nurse their infants, the suckling of the babies induces uterine contractions which facilitate the recovery from the birth process. It has long been known that some women are able to have and enjoy a breast orgasm while nursing their babies. The fact that nursing mothers enjoy varied genital pleasure during the suckling process is one of the largely-unacknowledged secrets of motherhood. I have conversed with mothers who mentioned multiple "suckling orgasms" while feeding their infants. Two described these climaxes as very intense, and in all but one instance distinctive uterine and/or vaginal/cervical contractions were noted at the peak of the experience.

Next to the clitoral orgasm, the breast orgasm seems to be the most widely recognized and acknowledged by women. This appears especially true of the older generation, many of whom report that in their youth, they were afraid to "go all the way" because of the moral restrictions of the time, or a fear of getting pregnant. Instead, they enjoyed extensive breast stimulation during heavy "petting" and "necking" sessions in which orgasm often took place.

Psychological factors associated with the breast orgasm

Although virtually all women are aware that their breasts are a major source of attraction for men, many women have ambivalent feelings about their breasts. They may be dissatisfied with the shape or size of their breasts, or be critical of the shape and size of their nipples. As a result, they may go through a bout of anxiety the first time they expose their naked breasts to a new lover. Not surprisingly then, loving attention paid to their breasts throughout the sex act constitutes a very powerful form of reassurance. The attention a man pays to a woman's breasts is his way of proclaiming her sexual attractiveness, and may allay her self-doubts by reinforcing her self-concept of being a desirable woman. ("During breast play, I very much enjoy being a woman. I really get into that.")

For some women, nipple stimulation not only fuels arousal, passion and desire, but appears to be less threatening than genital play. The same is true of the breast climax.

("It's a safer orgasm. There's no mess. I feel very intimate and complete, but I also want more.") For some women, the breast orgasm is a "purer" and "cleaner" climax.

On a deeper level, breast play and breast orgasm arouses maternal instincts and protective feelings toward a male partner. A man suckling or playing with a woman's breast is seen as non-threatening since he is now in what amounts to a dependent position. For some women, breast play and the breast climax create feelings of being in power or in charge. ("I'm on top of the world and can take care of everything—him, too.") Fleeting feelings—fantasies of wanting to mother the partner—may occur.

What women have to say about the breast orgasm

"I've had the ability to have a breast orgasm since I was a teenager. My first serious date used to bring me off by playing with my nipples. This was when I was sixteen."

I started masturbating at fourteen. I used my finger for the clitoral orgasm—it was much sharper. The breast one was fuller, more complete and somehow the clit seemed to be involved, too. The two orgasms were entirely different."

"Ever since I had my nipples pierced they are extremely sensitive. Now I have very powerful breast orgasms without other stimulation."

"I have the breast orgasm very rarely. It feels nice, sharp and delicious. The build-up is slow. Most guys get impatient. Men don't take time enough."

When it occurs, it's as if my body was summed up in just *that part*, the breasts. It's a feeling that makes me want more and at the same time to stop being stimulated. It starts in the breasts but I can feel it in the clit area, too. My mind is confused and my body tensed."

Study Findings
Of all women (205) from the Primary Group participating in this research, 29% (60) reported having breast orgasms.

The first three of the woman's Basic Seven have ben explored. The next chapter will cover the remaining four, including the G-Spot orgasm, whose existence is still doubted by some so-called experts.

Notes

1.   Joseph LoPiccolo and Leslie LoPiccolo, *Handbook of Sex Therapy,* (Plenum Press, 1978): 13.

2,   Avodah K. Offit, *The Sexual Self,* (J. B. Lippincott, 1977): 151.

3.   Mary Jane Sherfey, *The Nature and Evolution of Female Sexuality,* (Random House, 1972).

4.   William H. Masters, Virginia E. Johnson, Robert C. Kolodny, *Heterosexuality* (Harper Colins, 1992): 510

5.   Alice K. Ladas, Beverly Whipple and John D. Perry, *The G-Spot,* (C. Holt, Rinehart and Winston, 1982): 158

6.   Hanny Lightfoot-Klein, "The Sexual Experience and Marital Adjustment of Genitally Circumcised and Infibulated Females in the Sudan," *Journal of Sex Research,* 26 (1989): 375

7.   Zwi Hoch, "The Sensory Arm of the Female Orgasmic Reflex," *Journal of Sex Education and Sex Therapy* 6 (1980): 5

8.   Heli Alzate, "Vaginal Eroticism and Female Orgasm: A Current Appraisal, *Journal of Sex and Marital Therapy 11* (1985): 281.

9.   Gilbert Tordjman, "New realities in the Study of the Female Orgasms," *Journal of Sex Education and Sex Therapy 6* (1980): 24.

10.   Avodah K. Offit, op cit : 171.

CHAPTER 4

THE WOMAN'S BASIC SEVEN
PART II

In the previous chapter, the clitoral, vaginal/cervical and breast orgasms were explored—all of which are well-known. In this chapter, four more orgasms are covered: the mouth orgasm, G-Spot, and the anal and mental orgasms. Some of these are less known and others largely unknown to many sexologists and the general public. All of these, however, are available to many, if not all, women.

4. THE MOUTH ORGASM

The mouth orgasm happens at the peak of stimulation of the mouth, may begin in the mouth and/or throat and may expand from there. This type of orgasm appears to be more widespread than previously suspected and has been largely ignored by researchers. With the current growing interest in oral sex, however, the incidence of mouth orgasms can be expected to increase.

Why the mouth?
The mouth is a primary human sensory organ. For the infant and during the first years, it is the *most important* organ and the main source of sensual pleasure. The baby's mouth offers a source of in-touchness with the mother. Mommy is not only the source of food and love, but she represents the larger world. (Remember the stage when Baby puts every-thing into the mouth?) Erections—perhaps caused by the in-tense pleasure of sucking—have been reported in male ba-bies while they were at their mothers' breasts.

The mouth plays a primary role in the human sexual nervous system. It functions as a means of sexual communication level (kissing, tasting, etc.) The mouth orgasm appears to be triggered by the various component parts of the oral cavity—the lips, tongue, roof of the mouth and the throat. What part, or combination of parts, triggers the orgasm depends on the individual.

With some, the orgasm begins with highly pleasurable sensations in the lips, while others feel them in the roof of the mouth, etc. Some women climax while kissing; others view the mouth orgasm strictly as an *hors d'oeuvre* before the main course. Still other women experience a mouth orgasm while performing oral sex on a man.

Interviews revealed that some women were able to identify the parts of the mouth involved in the triggering of the orgasm. Intense feelings of pleasure usually began to build up in the lips. (There was no stimulation of other body parts at the time.) At the point of release, there was sometimes a whole body orgasm with shaking or contractions of different body parts. More often the climax was reported as spreading through the body and only subsequently centering in the genital area. Both vaginal and uterine contractions were reported. Some women stated that the orgasm moved from the mouth to the clitoris.

Finally, there is another variant of the mouth orgasm. A group of women, discovered in the course of interviews, *were able to have an orgasm while kissing.* Eight women reported having this orgasm while in their teens and at the peak of a kissing session. Three of the women reported currently having occasional orgasms while kissing. In two instances, sudden orgasms involving the total body took place in the midst of kissing. For the rest, the orgasm clearly began with special sensations in the lips.

Learning about the mouth orgasm

In the early days of my sex life, I was unaware that mouth orgasms existed. During Word War II, when in the U. S. Air Force, about thirty of us soldiers were taken by bus from Keesler Field in Biloxi, to a dance in a rural area of Mississippi. After the dance, my bunk mate told me that he and about a dozen other soldiers had, in his words, ". . . been sucked off by a cocksucker. She really enjoyed it and she must have come at least ten times."

For the next fifteen years, I was to hear numerous reports from friends and acquaintances about this oral phenomenon, but the Goddess Fortuna did not smile upon me until I was in my forties. After I had published my first book in the field of sexology, I noticed that most sexologists believed that the mouth orgasm was a figment of the imagination. We were, at the time, in the midst of the "women can only have clitoral orgasms" frenzy.

Several of my colleagues, on hearing me talk about mouth orgasms, had a very simple explanation. They said that while "giving head," these women were consciously (or unconsciously) compressing their thighs or rubbing their legs together, thus stimulating the clitoris and inducing climax. The mouth orgasm, they argued, was really a clitoral climax.

Over the years, I have had the opportunity to personally observe four instances of women having an oral orgasm while fellating. In three out of four cases, the legs of the women were well separated while "giving head," thus negating the hypothesis that the clitoris was involved. (The fourth woman's legs were together during fellatio and there was some ecstatic squirming during the orgasm. She *said* she did not exert pressure on her clitoris with her thighs, but unconscious self-stimulation remains a possibility.) All four women mentioned they had mouth orgasms of considerable intensity. Two described it as similar to an "electric current" beginning in the mouth and taking over the rest of the body. One said: "It came on suddenly and feels the same as my other whole body orgasms."

In 1982, my notebooks have an entry indicating that I met two women who talked about their mouth orgasms. In both cases, the mouth orgasm took place while orally stimulating their lovers' breasts. One woman was heterosexual, one lesbian. For the former, it was her first mouth orgasm. She said she and her lover had been separated, due to circumstances, for almost a month. She had no sex in the interim. When they got together— "He asked me to suck his nipples. I got so much into it, I couldn't stop. My lips and palate started to vibrate and there was a total body orgasm."

Psychological factors associated with the mouth orgasm

Very rarely does a description of oral sex encompass *how this sex act feels to the mouth of the practitioner.* Instead, the focus is more often on the recipient of oral sex than on the stimulation experienced by the one who is giving it. When a woman places her mouth on a man's penis, she may feel a sense of power—she may feel he is totally in her control, at least for the moment. Conscious or unconscious replications of nipple play and the pleasure of total concentration on suckling are also reported. ("For a while, I do it just like a baby.")

For some women, feelings of subjugation and/or pleasure from doing something forbidden, taboo, or "dirty" may emerge. Others fantasize that they are being forced to perform oral sex, or that they are submissive to—or dominated by— the man, the thought of which arouses their passions. The mouth orgasm, in some women, develops particularly strong feelings of closeness and lovingness. "When I come (orally) at the same time he comes in my mouth, I feel closer to him than ever before.")

How does a mouth orgasm feel?

The intensity of the mouth orgasm varies. For some it is a highly intense experience, for others it is less charged. Then there are those women who find the mouth orgasm deeply satisfying, but also enjoy other climaxes. Yet another group of women interviewed reported that they find the mouth orgasm so satisfying that they prefer it to all other ways of climaxing and that "giving head" is their sole means of having sex. They usually orgasm when the man does. Although *vox populi* dubs these women as "cocksuckers," a less pejorative term is <u>oral orgiasts</u>.

An extensive, in-depth study of the oral orgiast, both male and female, who exclusively and routinely have mouth orgasms (without any genital stimulation) needs to be under-

taken. Research with this group would probably yield significant additional insights about the nature of all human orgasms. I am hoping to find sufficient interest among colleagues
to organize a team to do research in this area some time after
the year 2000. (Interested colleagues, please contact me.)

The following descriptions of mouth orgasms were, in
part, transcribed from interviews.

"I come off and have a complete orgasm that way without
touching myself. My mouth starts to tingle—more and
more, then my whole body gets into it. It doesn't happen all the time—maybe half the time.It works better if
I'm turned on or completely free of inhibition."

"Basically, I would describe the mouth orgasms as an
opening, deeply allowing the roof of my mouth to connect
with the top of my head and beyond. The back of my
throat stretches to the back of my neck and I feel timeless, boundaryless, in a state of total delight and surrender."

"There is a tingling, an erotic sensation which builds and
builds in the lining of the mouth. I come when he comes.
After the orgasm, the tingling sensation comes down
gradually like in a clitoral orgasm."

"It's not localized in my mouth, gets the whole body vibrating. I can feel the contractions in the vagina."

Study Findings

*Of all women (205) from the Primary Group participat-
ing in this research, 20% (41) reported having mouth orgasms.*

5. THE G-SPOT ORGASM

The G-Spot, or Grafenberg Spot, orgasm happens at the peak of stimulation of a sensitive spot at the anterior wall of the vagina. The climax may begin at the G-spot and may expand from there.

What is a G-spot? Where is it located?

This erotically sensitive spot is usually described as located between the eleven and two o'clock position on the vaginal barrel. In many women, it is approximately halfway between the cervix and the back of the pubic bone, on the upper wall of the vagina. The size of the G-Spot varies from the approximate dimension of a hazel nut to the full breadth of the middle two fingers. On arousal, the spot usually increases in size. It is often a small node which swells when stimulated. However, deeper and stronger stimulation of the G-Spot, as opposed to the clitoris, is required to bring most women to orgasm.

The sexologist Dr. Heli Alzate believes that there may be two other erogenous spots at four o'clock and eight o'clock on the vaginal barrel. I would agree with Dr. Alzate that some women have several sensitive spots or erotic zones present in the vagina. Others have only one such spot, and still others appear to have none. There are also some women who have the G-Spot, but who may not be aware of it.

Who discovered the G-Spot?

The G-Spot was discovered in 1944 by two specialists in obstetrics and gynecology. The German physician Ernst Grafenberg and his American colleague Robert Dickinson described their discovery as " . . . a zone of erogenous feeling . . . located along the suburethral surface of the anterior vaginal wall." (1) Grafenberg again published this finding in 1950. Sexologist John Heidenry however, points out that the Dutch physician Regnier de Graaf first mentioned female ejaculation in 1672, with Western medical books subsequently making numerous references to this phenomenon since that time. (2)

Then, in 1982, three American sexologists—Ladas, Whipple and Perry—published their breakthrough book, *The G-Spot*, (Holt, Rhinehart, Winston) in which they asserted that the G-Spot does indeed exist, and that the orgasm it produces is different from the orgasm produced by stimulation of the clitoris. Ever since the publication of this important book, the G-Spot has become embroiled in controversy. (3)

Initially, sexologists Masters and Johnson denied the existence of the G-Spot. They attacked and ridiculed reports that some women had an ejaculation from stimulating this area of the vagina, and denounced the G-Spot researchers. More than ten years later, however, Masters and Johnson were forced to publicly admit not only the existence of the G-Spot, but its ejaculatory capacities. Repeated studies have determined there can be an ejaculation of a non-urinary fluid resulting from stimulation of this area.

It took almost fifteen years for sexologists to become aware of additional grave research errors in the work of Masters and Johnson. For the excellent critique of their research, psychologists Michael Evans and Bernie Zilbergeld deserve a vote of thanks. These clinicians, in an article in *Psychology Today,* concluded that "Masters and Johnson's sex-therapy research is so flawed by methodological errors and slipshod reporting that it fails to meet customary standards—and their own—for evaluations." (4) People are largely unaware of this realistic assessment.

Surprisingly, in their most recent book, *Heterosexuality* (HarperCollins, 1994) Masters and Johnson reversed their position about the G-Spot once again. In this volume, which was co-authored with Robert Kolodny, *none* of the diagrams of the female genitalia reveal the presence of the G-Spot, nor is this orgasm source listed in the index. Rather, the authors' belief in *clitorocentrism* is once again asserted.

Why do women have a G-spot?
No one really knows for certain, but medical research published in 1984 concluded that the G-Spot is the female equivalent of the prostate gland in the male. (5) The two or-

gans are similar in many ways. There are those who think it may be vestigial, i.e. a "hold-over" from a previous phase of female genital evolution. This might explain why some women cannot locate theirs. However, if the G-Spot has any particular biological function other than as a source of sexual stimulation, what that function may be has not as yet been determined.

The G-Spot is not a "new invention." It has been known to other cultures in the past, since the first century A. D.. The Chinese called this erotically sensitive area "the black pearl," and it was known to the Japanese as the "skin of the earthworm." (6)

How does the G-Spot feel when stimulated?

When the G-Spot is first stimulated (by one or two fingers), many women feel as if they are about to urinate, since this area lies in the vascular tissue surrounding the urethra. (This keeps many women from exploring the G-Spot orgasm.) *However, with continued stimulation, this urge to void may gradually disappear, being replaced by strong feelings of sexual pleasure*, culminating in orgasm. Some, but not all, women may have an ejaculation of fluids at the time of climax. These fluids are *not* urine. There are videos of this type of ejaculation.

Many women find that, during intercourse, the G-Spot is most easily stimulated by the "woman on top" or "woman superior" position. Others prefer the rear-entry position, while they are on their hands and knees, or on their stomachs, or their sides. (It helps to arch the back and create the precise angle for maximum stimulation of the spot.)

The sex toy industry is banking on a growing number of women exploring their G-Spot. A special vibrator has been developed exclusively for G-Spot stimulation. It is now commercially available in sex shops or "adult" emporiums.

Psychological factors associated with the G-Spot orgasm

Despite the availability of books and articles on the subject, many women are still in the dark about the existence, location and pleasure to be derived from the G-Spot. Others, who have heard that it exists, do not attempt to locate it, or make plans to use it during sex. As a result, for many women, the G-Spot orgasm has not as yet emerged as a separate climactic experience.

For some, their minds actually set up psychological barriers to the G-Spot. The sexologist Lonnie Barbach, in her book *For Each Other*, reports instances of women so embarrassed by their ejaculation of fluid during orgasm that they totally inhibited their climax. (7) Others underwent surgery to control "urinary incontinence," although emission of fluid occurred only at the moment of orgasm. Although weakness of the pubococcygeal muscle can result in urinary incontinence, the women who underwent surgery were found to have strong "PC" muscles.

Without a doubt, the combination of the urge to urinate plus the fear of ejaculation can result in the formation of strong psychological barriers which prevent women from becoming intimate with the G-Spot. There is nothing romantic about "wetting the bed." On the other hand, some fortunate women have partners who understand that the ejaculation is not urine, and who welcome this warm stream of fluid as evidence that a woman is "really turned on."

More experiences with the G-Spot

I first became acquainted with the G-Spot during the latter part of the forties, when I was a graduate student at Tulane University. A friend, who was a television personality, often talked to me about the orgasms of his wife, who had ejaculations so copious that they routinely used rubber sheets during intercourse. (Conversation with his wife confirmed this phenomenon.)

Later in my life, two of my companions had G-Spot ejaculations. With one person, they were occasional and she said she had no control over them. She at first thought the fluid was urine, but this proved not to be the case. I always enjoyed the warm feelings of the jetting fluid bathing my genitals. At the time, I thought the emission was due to the excessive production of the Bartholin glands which lie within the inner lips, or labia minora, since no one had ever heard of a G-Spot.

My second companion with G-Spot emissions lived with me for a number of years. During the "honeymoon" phase of our relationship (which lasted about six months), she, like my friend's wife, would also have copious ejaculations. I again assigned this to the Bartholin glands, but the phenomenon totally disappeared after a year and a half and never recurred for the remainder of our time together.

What women have to say about the G-Spot orgasm

Reports of how the G-Spot orgasm feels vary. Some find the climax to be different but less pleasurable than other types of orgasms. For others, it is superior to and more intense than the clitoral climax.

> "At first it felt like I had to go to the bathroom, but it then just sort of let go. It [the orgasm] felt better than the others."

> "My first G-Spot orgasm is still very vivid in my mind and it still excites me to recall it. I had briefly heard of the G-Spot but never experienced it. The orgasm occurred in a threesome situation—my husband, one of our single male friends and myself. While being fingered by our friend while my breasts being massaged by my husband, our friend massaged my G-Spot and it wasn't long before I had a very wild orgasm. A very pleasurable warm sensation overtook me and an almost total blackout feeling overcame me. I experienced a tunnel effect—the surroundings became distant and I became completely relaxed, yet aware."

> "My feelings are that of total elation, my whole body feels like it's on fire before I reach a peak and then at the peak it's a feeling of total titillation and serenity consuming me at the same time. What a wonderful, satisfying experience!"

Women who experience the distinct G-Spot orgasm report increased feelings of self-worth and sexual self-confidence. They find it satisfying to have acquired a new source of sexual enjoyment and satisfaction. Some women who ejaculate on orgasm find this to be a new source of empowerment, as well, since their partners view them as unusually responsive in bed. The vast majority of U. S. women appear not to have discovered this type of climax, as yet.

Study Findings

Of all women (205) from the Primary Group participating in this research, 33% (68) reported having G-Spot orgasms.

6. THE ANAL ORGASM

The anal orgasm happens at the height of stimulation of the anal area, it may begin in the anal area and expand from there. Due to cultural conditioning as well as the fear of AIDS, this appears to be the least acceptable orgasm to women. There are some indications, however, that an increasing number of women are experimenting with this type of intercourse since it adds new dimensions of variety to the orgasmic experience. Interest in the anal orgasm can be expected to grow slowly but surely stronger, accelerating after the first quarter of the new century when most of today's older generation have passed on.

Why the anus?

Since women come equipped with a natural sexual orifice—the vagina— why do some of them gravitate to anal intercourse as well? One reason is that there are clusters of highly sensitive nerves around the rim and entrance of the anal sphincter. These can provide new erotic sensations. For some women, the perineum—the area between the anus and the vaginal opening—is also erogenous. Many women enjoy finger stimulation of the anus before or during intercourse.

During anal intercourse itself, the rhythmic pounding from the in-and-out motion of the penis generates vibrations and conveys stimulation to the adjacent area. As a result, the sensitive nerve clusters around the cervix and uterus are stimulated as well. Some physicians believe that stimulation of the pubococcygeal muscles during anal intercourse also triggers orgasmic response.

How does anal sex feel?

Provided the sphincter is sufficiently relaxed (and lubricated), penetration of the anus is reported, by many, to be highly exciting and pleasurable. The presence of the penis in the rectum causes a feeling of pleasurable fullness.

The interior of the rectum is sufficiently sensitive to distinguish between a cold and warm infusion of liquids, such as in an enema. There is a firm basis, then, for women who describe a sensation of warmth inside the rectum at the time of male ejaculation. Afficionados of anal sex praise both the tightness and higher temperature of the orifice.

The anal sex taboo and the risk factor associated with the practice

A very strong taboo against anal sex exists in most Western cultures. Powerful feelings of repulsion, disgust and shame about body waste products and their elimination are routinely induced in children. The negative attitudes and feelings about defecation, urination and the passing of gas are very deeply implanted and strongly conditioned. For some, these negative attitudes are so strong they make all sex less pleasurable. *This type of toxicity prohibits most women (and men) from utilizing the anal area as a sexual pleasure zone throughout their lives.* (See Chapter 5, pp. 89-95).

The risk associated with anal sex has increased since the advent of AIDS. Since a significant majority of AIDS victims are homosexual men, many of whom engage in anal intercourse, this form of sexual pleasure has become even more suspect. Paradoxically, at the same time, heterosexual men and women (as well as lesbians) appear to make increasing use of this practice.

Unprotected anal sex can indeed be risky. Minute tears may develop in the intestinal walls during intercourse, or the woman may have fissures or sore spots in her rectum. Not only does she risk infection, but if her partner is bisexual with careless sex practices, she may risk acquiring the HIV virus. If the tongue comes into contact with fecal matter, there may be an infection by disease such as hepatitis. Finally, it is very important to guard against infection by washing the penis immediately after anal coitus to prevent transferring bacteria from the rectum into the vagina, or mouth.

Anal intercourse has not been universally taboo in all cultures. It was widely practiced in ancient Greece and Rome and numerous other societies. According to one scholar:

"There are innumerable passages in Greek and Roman literature proving several points about anal intercourse. First, it was extremely popular; second, that women neither resented it nor opposed it but found it a particularly stimulating form of love-making, as it was apt to produce multiple orgasm by the combination of simultaneous manual love-play and coitus; and finally, that it was never considered a perversion, but as one of the principal methods to prevent conception." (8)

Psychological factors associated with anal sex

Because of the proximity of the excretory organs to the reproductive organs, feelings of repulsion and disgust are often associated with—or transferred to—the genitals. As a consequence, the sex organs and sex acts are widely seen as being "dirty." While this attitude can impair sexual functioning and the quality of the orgasm in any type of sex that includes genital contact, it is most prevalent vis-a-vis anal sex. As one woman put it: "I know I shouldn't, but I keep feeling it's all dirty down there."

Gradations of this attitude—ranging from mild trepidation to out-and-out disgust—are common. Therefore it is not surprising that, for many women, the idea of anal stimulation or penetration evokes strong feelings of being soiled or even degraded. For others, a religious taboo is added, making the practice a sin.

For some women, anal sex becomes the "ultimate invasion of privacy," or "a violation of intimacy." Conversely, there can also be feelings of offering, or opening up, hidden parts of the self to a lover. This can lead to more profound intimacy, since it involves lowering or removing a former barrier to personal closeness.

Some women describe the anal orgasm as being the strongest and most intense they have experienced. This may reflect a lack of anxiety related to the threat of conception. It may also reflect pride in overcoming the attitude that "anal sex is dirty." The alleged "sinfulness" or "badness" of the act may also add spice. Finally, the novelty and new erotic sen-sations of the practice may serve to fuel passion. The best book for those interested in exploring the erotic potential of the anus is sexologist Jack Morin's *Anal Pleasure and Health* Down There Press, 1998 third edition.

How prevalent is anal intercourse for women?

David Bolling, an OB/GYN Texas physician, has published a number of papers about female anal intercourse. He concludes that "about one fourth of American women occasionally engage in anal intercourse," and that 10% of all women engage in this type of sex regularly, for pleasure. He also found that 50% of the "active pleasurable anal intercourse users" achieved orgasm through the act. In his 1987 study of 1,000 healthy gynecological patients, Dr. Bolling found that 723 women had tried anal intercourse and 238 (24%) women found it a pleasurable source of sex. (9)

The well known author, Nancy Friday, in her 1991 book, *Women On Top*, shared an interesting observation. While interviewing young women for her book, she noted "the eager curiosity and lack of hesitancy the women show in exploring anal sex." (10) In 1994, June Reinisch, the director of the Kinsey Institute, summarized new research data about the incidence of anal intercourse by U. S. women in her book, *The Kinsey Institute New Report On Sex* (St. Martin's Press). In an effort to determine the number of women who have experienced anal intercourse at least once, seven studies conducted over the past forty years were surveyed. Reinisch concludes:

"Our conservative estimate is that 33 percent—or more than one in three—have done so. In a recent study by the Kinsey Institute of college students at a midwestern university, almost 24 percent of the women and 27 percent of the men reported having tried anal inter-course at least once." (11)

According to Reinisch, by the mid-nineties, 30-40% of American women will have had anal intercourse. In my own life, I have known two women who told me that their anal orgasms, compared to other types of orgasms, were the most intense. In both instances, these women enjoyed clitoral and vaginal orgasms, although anal intercourse was preferred. One woman routinely gave herself an enema prior to intercourse. She would sometimes have an orgasm while doing this.

In the course of interviews with women about their orgasms, a small number (eight) mentioned achieving a climax from a practice they called either "tonguing" or "anolingus." This erotic technique involves the use of the tongue by their partner, to stimulate the partner's anus. Some reported the tongue was inserted into the anus. It is clear, however, that the area around the woman's anal sphincter— similar to the man's— is very rich in sensitive nerve endings which enable women to have an anal orgasm solely from stimulation of the sphincter. Lesbian literature is replete with descriptions of orgasms achieved by women through anolingual stimulation.

A few years ago, I met a highly educated and successful attorney and businesswoman at a cocktail party. On hearing that I was sexologist, she insisted on confiding her recent sex history. She was 38 years old, and, until recently, had never had an orgasm. She had been married for ten years, had divorced, and then had enjoyed a number of lovers. Her latest lover had introduced her to anal sex. She had an "earth shattering" anal orgasm, involving her whole body ("It was like a seizure.") She believed that because of this experience, she would ultimately be able to have other types of orgasms, as well.

What women have to say about anal orgasms

"The first time I had anal intercourse, I came that way. My lover was a very caring person and took a long time preparing me for it. First he used one finger, then two, plenty of lubricant and talked very lovingly while doing it. I came and it felt completely different from any other orgasmic experience—I mean masturbation or normal intercourse. It was a totally complete orgasm. I felt marvelous afterwards."

"It is stronger than the vaginal—more localized. But not as strong as the clitoral."

"There are contractions in the anal area and a total body orgasm involving the vagina."

"I have had a couple of anal orgasms that were different because of the pain/pleasure combination, which was very satisfying, but only with the right partner."

"The secret is that either you push against the penis with your ass,or you push out as if you are having a bowel movement, while he enters very slowly. He should pause when fully in. The woman then begins to move when she's ready. The climax is terrific."

The distinctive quality and nature of the anal climax makes it, in the words of one woman, "a very special and loving kind of climax for both of us." Some women are aware that coming to grips with the complex of negative feelings and beliefs associated with the anal area constitute a major breakthrough in their personal and sexual development. A sense of pride of accomplishment and a new sense of freedom are usually the result of overcoming the anal taboo. In November 1998, the state of Georgia dismissed its laws against sodomy—a "straw in the wind"?

Study Findings
Of all women (205) from the Primary Group participating in this research, 9% (18) reported having anal orgasms.

7. THE MENTAL ORGASM

There are two types of mental orgasms—the externally triggered and the inner directed. *The mental orgasm sometimes happens at the peak of external stimuli such as phone calls, photographs, or films. It may also be inner directed, occurring at the peak of stimulation through sexual fantasies which focus on achieving orgasm.* Sometimes such an orgasm takes place in a woman's dreams. In all instances, the mental climax occurs without touching the genitalia.

In February, 1987, while walking through a swap meet in Orange, California, I discovered a book on the use of corporal discipline in education, based on the work of the Vienna Institute for Sexual Research, and published in 1932. In the concluding portion of the book, there is a statement which indicates that European sexologists, more than fifty years ago, were aware of the mental orgasm. "... there is thought onanism, or psychic onanism (during) which, solely on the basis of images, that is, without help of manual stimulation, sexual excitation and orgasm is induced." (Translation) (12)

How rare is it?
Based on his research, Alfred Kinsey concluded that only 2% of women were capable of an orgasm from fantasy alone. In my own research, however, I found this figure to be closer to a fourth of the sexually-active female participants in the Orgasm Research Spectrum study. Sexologist Gina Ogden, in her 1994 book, *Women Who Love Sex,* concluded "that "sixty-four percent of the women in the original research study said they were able to experience orgasm 'spontaneously' without any physical touch at all . . ." (13)

In 1992, a study by sexologists Beverly Whipple, Gina Ogden and Barry Komisaruk established that women are capable of having an "imagery induced orgasm" without touch-

77

ing the body." The researchers concluded that "During orgasms induced only by imagery, women can manifest all of the physiological events that we measured of a magnitude comparable to those during orgasms produced by genital stimulation. Presently, there is a monolithic model of orgasm based on the sexual response cycle, which involves a physical stimulus (Masters and Johnson, 1966). Sex therapy and sex education are based on this model. *Since the present study provides evidence that orgasm can also be generated by non-physical stimulation, a reassessment of the nature of orgasm is warranted.*" (14) Emphasis added.

Gina Ogden, in her book, refers to the imagery as "thinking off." Although mental orgasms do not appear to be common, the use of fantasy for arousal and/or to enhance the sex experience is anything *but* rare. Sexual fantasies are routinely used by both men and women as a means of erotic arousal, for masturbatory purposes, and as a way to facilitate the process of moving toward climax. Researchers have found that in normal married women, sexual fantasies and daydreams are widely used. Their use does not indicate interpersonal disturbances, adjustment problems, or lack of sexual fulfillment.

An extensive study published in 1986 revealed that 88% of married women had occasional sexual fantasies, mostly while daydreaming. Another study of sixty easily-orgasmic women by sexologists Marc and Judith Meshorer, revealed that 80-90% of them used fantasy in some form, including erotic imaging. (15) Some women use sexual fantasies during intercourse to attain an orgasm. While making love, they may utilize mental images of movie stars or former lovers.

A number of well-known sexologists (among them L. Barbach, A. Ladas, B. Whipple and J. Perry) have gone on record to state that some women can have orgasms from fantasies alone. This was also discussed in the original Kinsey report, but has largely been ignored. Kinsey's research revealed that women who fantasize during sex are more than twice as likely to be college educated than those who do not, *with only women capable of the fantasy orgasm.* Some sexologists, in the past, have variously attributed a mental orgasm to a woman's "hysteria," prevarication, or a "sick imagination."

My own research indicates that fantasy-triggered mental orgasms are more easily achieved (*by both genders*) when there has been a period of abstinence. At such times, a greater mental and emotional readiness for this type of orgasm exists. Women become aware of specific sexual tensions in their bodies, or in their genital regions (which is also the case with men.) This appears to create an additional readiness for an orgasm created solely by the mind.

On a physiological level, the mental orgasm does not appear to differ from the others. The normal signs of sexual excitation can usually be observed. As the point of orgasm approaches, the heart rate increases, breathing becomes more rapid, the genitals tumesce just as if *physical arousal* were taking place. Physical arousal *is* actually taking place, but without benefit of hands or genitals.

Mental orgasms from external stimuli

The external stimuli may consist of sexually-arousing scenes from films, from photographs, or from the human voice conveying sexually-exciting messages. Numerous women reported climaxing during a phone call from their lovers after lengthy separations. On being exposed to such stimuli, a woman may orgasm without touching any of her erogenous zones. Does the external stimulus trigger the orgasm? No, the internal, subjective processes of fantasizing, coupled with a state of readiness bring the result.

Surprisingly, some woman have a totally different perspective of what took place. They may insist that the stimulus was solely responsible for the orgasm. "(It really turned me on and made me come to hear his voice saying those things.") Thus the responsibility for the climax is placed outside the self, by trying to deny that the mind made it happen. These women either find the power of their own mind hard to believe, or are trying to find a "logical reason" for this manifestation of their sexual power.

A highly successful woman in industry, whom I have known for years, had a lover who did considerable traveling. He would call her and, as she put it, "sex talk to me." While he was doing this, she would get sexually aroused and climax without touching herself. She told me "it felt like my normal orgasms—super!"

The inner-directed mental orgasm

Again, there is no physical stimulation of any erogenous zones. Instead, the inner-directed type of mental orgasm is created within the psyche by the imagination, which projects erotic fantasies on the screen of the mind. Usually, the orgasm occurs as a result of a specific set of fantasies. In most such instances, the woman does not attribute her climax to any external source. Rather, she claims total responsibility for achieving it solely by using her mental powers.

It is not always possible to maintain control over inner-directed orgasms. The types of interference most often mentioned are noises and distractions (such as the ringing of a telephone), recent orgasmic release (low sexual hunger), fatigue, and "difficulty getting into the mood" to have an inner-directed climax.

What women say about their mental orgasm

"When I am horny, I can close my eyes and use my fantasy. I fantasize about past scenes with one of my lovers and always come in two minutes. The orgasm is very special, intense and fairly long. Leaves me totally relaxed."

"When I read letters in *Penthouse* or in the *Forum,* I can have an orgasm without touching myself. It's different— long-lasting and concentrated in the vagina. I get very wet."

"Usually I have a rape fantasy. My feeling of helplessness tends to enhance and increase the orgasm which seems to begin in the general area of the uterus (midbelly) and spread from there."

"While reading very sexual books, I insert myself into them and share experiences—usually to orgasm."

The ability to produce a mental orgasm is an excellent subject for further research. There may be far more women than we know who have this ability—and use it. However, many such women may be reluctant to admit to having this capability, perhaps in the fear that they will be thought of as "oversexed."

Study Findings

Of all women (205) from the Primary Group participating in this research, 24% (50) reported having mental orgasms.

This concludes the review of the Woman's Basic Seven climaxes. In the following chapter, the man's Six Basic Orgasms will be explored in detail.

Notes

1. Ernst Grafenberg and Robert L. Dickinson, "Conception Control by Plastic Cervix Cap," *Western Journal of Surgery, Obstetrics and Gynecology*, 52 (1944): 335-340.

2. John Heidenry, *What Wild Ecstasy*, (Simon & Schuster, 1997): 301-302.

3. Alice K. Ladas, Beverly Whipple and John D. Perry, *The G-Spot*, (Holt, Rhinehart and Winston, 1982).

4. Philip Nobile, "Interview: Dr. Bernie Zilbergeld," *Penthouse Forum Magazine*, (June, 1983): 14-15.

5. Desmond Heath, "An Investigation Into the Origins of a Copious Vaginal Discharge During Intercourse: Enough to Wet the Bed—That is not Urine." *The Journal of Sex Research*, 20 (1984): 206.

6. Alice K. Ladas, "The G-Spot Revisited," *Women's News*, September, 1985: 19.

7. Lonnie Barbach, *For Each Other*, (Anchor Press, Doubleday, 1982): 67.

8. Paul Tabort, *The Humor and Technology of Sex*, (Julian Press, 1969): 470.

9. David Bolling, an unpublished paper entitled "Heterosexual Anal Intercourse: A Common Entity, Perceived Rarity, Neglect of Patients and an Ostrich Syndrome," presented at the Kinsey Institute, 1987.

10. Nancy Friday, *Women On Top*, (Simon & Schuster, 1991): 355.

11. June Reinisch, *The Kinsey Institute New Report On Sex*, (St. Martin's Press, 1990): 137.

12. Heinrich Worenkam and Gertrude Perkauf, *Erziehungs—Flagellantismus,* (Verlag fur Kulturforschung, 1932): 190.

13. Gina Ogden, *Women Who Love Sex,* (Pocket Books, 1994): 22.

14. Beverly Whipple, Gina Ogden and Barry Komisaruk, "Physiological Correlates of Imagery—Induced Orgasm in Women," *Archives of Sexual Behavior*, 21 (1992): 121-133.

15. Marc and Judith Meshorer, *Ultimate Pleasure*, (St. Martin's Press, 1986): 180.

Resources

Tristan Taormino, *The Ultimate Guide to Anal Sex for Women*, Cleis Press, San Francisco ($14.95).

CHAPTER 5

THE MAN'S BASIC SIX

Until quite recently, it was widely believed that a man was capable of only one type of climax—the penile orgasm. The evidence now indicates that men are capable of a much wider range of orgasmic experiences. Every man has the *potential* to experience six distinct types of orgasms. The man's basic six are: 1) the penile orgasm, 2) the prostate orgasm, 3) the anal orgasm, 4) the breast orgasm, 5) the oral or mouth orgasm, and 6) the mental orgasm. Each of these climaxes will be discussed in detail in this chapter.

In addition, men are also capable of experiencing the fusion orgasm and the zone orgasm. (These are discussed in Chapter 6, pp. 107-113). It is little known that men are also capable of multiple orgasms. They are discussed in the initial section of this chapter.

MALE MULTIPLE ORGASMS AND VARIANTS

There is an erroneous belief that the man is capable of only one orgasm at a time, and must undergo a refractory, i.e. recovery period before the next one. However a number of research studies have shattered this myth by revealing that orgasm and ejaculation are *separate processes*, not one continuous process as was formerly believed. In the male multiple orgasm cycle, there is no refractory period following each orgasm, because *ejaculation* is postponed until the final climax. The erection is thus maintained, although there may be some lessening in penile tumescence.

In the multi-orgasmic sequence, there are a series of consecutive orgasms, with the ejaculatory orgasm usually experienced as being the most intense. According to researchers Robbins and Jensen, their subjects reported 3-10 orgasms per lovemaking session, *prior* to ejaculation. They propose the following explanation for the multiple orgasmic response:

> "Possibly the multiple orgasmic response is achieved by conscious or unconscious control or inhibition of movement of the ejaculate . . .Although it has been said that the relaxation of the external sphincter of the bladder is involuntary (Masters and Johnson, 1966), *perhaps this can be brought under voluntary control.* Without relaxation of the sphincter, the seminal fluid would not flow into the urethral bulb and penile urethra." (1) Emphasis added.

The writer has been multi-orgasmic for over fifteen years. This ability was discovered while I was training myself to prolong intercourse without ejaculation. The multiple orgasm, in my experience, differs in both quality and intensity and my tendency has been to treat it as a lesser climax, when it is merely *different.* These multiple climaxes occurred so routinely that I did not inform my loving companions for many years. At that time, I also refrained from vocalizing during the orgasm, for fear of triggering an ejaculation. This fear subsequently disappeared.

Quite a number of men may be multi-orgasmic without knowing it. They may have "dry orgasms" with no ejaculation (which, for some, may feel less intense, but "different"), not realizing that this is one hallmark of being multi-orgasmic. Nevertheless, training is required before the average male can routinely experience multi-orgasmic climaxes.

A variant of the multiple orgasm appears to be the extended male climax described by Alan and Donna Brauer in their book, *ESO, The Extended Sexual Orgasm.* The book contains detailed exercises which, if faithfully followed, promise the reader an extension in the length of his orgasm.

"Male orgasm ordinarily consists of two phases: an

emission phase lasting three to five seconds, followed by a sense of ejaculatory urgency and then an ejaculation phase of approximately ten contractions lasting about ten seconds. In Phase I, ESO, the emission phase is extended—to one minute, to ten minutes or more—followed by an intense but not necessarily extended ejaculation phase. Men experience this phase subjectively as sustained orgasmic pleasure . . .

At the highest level of male ESO, Phase II, a man finds himself in a continuous state of orgasmic emission for thirty minutes or more. Clear fluid issues almost continuously, drop by drop, from his penis." (2)

Sexologists William Hartman and Marilyn Fithian also researched the male multiorgasm, and co-authored their landmark book entitled *Any Man Can.* They concluded that 12% of the men they studied were multi-orgasmic. (3)

The latest book on the subject is Mantak Chia and Douglas Abrams Arava's *The Multi-Orgasmic Man,* (Harper San Francisco, 1996). The volume offers a detailed Taoist program to help the male become multi-orgasmic. It includes numerous and detailed muscular exercises to achieve this.

A final variant of the male orgasm must be mentioned. It is the whole body orgasm. Both men and women are capable of experiencing this type of climax. I have previously described some examples which have taken place in a spiritual context. (See Chapter 6, pp. 119-120 for a more detailed discussion.)

1. THE PENILE ORGASM

The penile orgasm happens at the peak of penile stimulation, seems to begin in the penis and may expand from there. For the vast majority of men, the penile orgasm is the only type of climax experienced during a lifetime of sex <u>because they do not know they have other orgasm options</u>. The penile orgasm will continue to dominate in the near future. However, an ever-increasing number of men will report experiencing the four other types of climaxes of which they are capable, plus the fusion and zone orgasm. By the first third of the new millennium, most men will be able to experience other orgasms in addition to the penile climax.

Understanding the physiology of the penile climax

The climactic process occurs in two phases. It begins with the intense stimulation of the glans, or head, and the rest of the penis. During this first, or *emission* phase, the stimulation is transmitted to the ejaculation center in the spinal cord, at which point the accessory organs of reproduction propel the seminal fluid substrate into the prostatic urethral bulb. Then, in the second or *expulsion* phase, the fluid moves from the urethral bulb through the membranous and penile segments of the urethra and is expelled by rhythmic contractions.

The *amount* of seminal fluid being ejaculated appears, for many men, to be related to the ecstasy experienced and the length of orgasm. (This is not true for all men and becomes less relevant with the advancing years.) The muscular contractions which accompany the expulsion of the ejaculate also seem to increase orgasmic pleasure.

Men of advanced years have consistently reported that the diminishing amount of ejaculate which many experience does not necessarily mean a diminution of peak ecstasy. The climax may feel different, but is as intense and satisfying. *The man's belief system about this change is the important variable.*

The force of the ejaculation appears to vary with age. In some men, the semen is expelled for three or more feet. Most men, however, report that their seminal fluid is ejaculated with relatively little force, traveling only a few inches or just oozing out of the urethra. Factors such as health, age, mood, energy level, period of abstinence since last emission, and degree of sexual stimulation all influence the strength and force of the male ejaculation.

The emission of ejaculate seems to be largely an autonomous reflex; men usually know when they have reached "the point of no return." At this juncture in the orgasm cycle, they can no longer control the emission unless, as previously mentioned, they have had training in how to delay it.

Immediately following ejaculation, the glans or head of the penis may be hypersensitive to pressure or touch. This may indicate the beginning of the *refractory period* experienced by most men—a period of recovery required for nerves and receptors before the penis is ready for action once again.

Psychological factors associated with the penile orgasm

Two psychologically-based hazards lurk in the background of the sexually active male's sex life. An encounter with either of these hazards—premature ejaculation and insufficient erection—can affect the quality of intercourse and orgasm.

Premature ejaculation occurs when a man ejaculates either before entering the vagina or shortly thereafter (definitions vary). According to some experts, as high as 40% of men have, at some time, had this problem. Especially when a man is young and virile, premature ejaculation can cause anxiety and noticeably affect his enjoyment of the climax (not to mention that of his partner.)

The inability to achieve or sustain an erection can be even more upsetting, since men are well aware that *will power cannot bring about an erect penis.* Many men do not know this. Erection is not within the man's conscious control—*he cannot make it happen,* except by using erection-causing drug Viagra. Most men have, at some time, suffered the embarassment of a limp penis when circumstances called for an erection. Even more deflating to the self-image is losing the erection during intercourse.

For many men, the penile orgasm is associated with feelings of strength and power and "being in control." Other men find that the climax means the giving up of control, giving over power and becoming dependent and child-like. Still others experience the orgasm as a form of fusion into a state of oneness with the partner. Quite often there is a combination of these varied feelings with each climax.

How a man interprets the meaning of his orgasm may influence both the intensity and quality of his climax. Some men, for example, perceive intercourse and orgasm as acts of hygiene (through the draining of excessive seminal fluid), or as a means of tension and release and relaxation. Most of these men may fall into a profound slumber immediately following the climax. For other men, sex is a form of celebration or renewal. They may feel energized after intercourse.

A "macho man" may feel that coitus is a way of exercising and displaying his masculine strength. Intercourse could also mean dominating or conquering a "weaker vessel," with sex becoming an act of raw power. ("I pounded the shit out of her—and did she love it!") From the macho perspective, the force or strength not only of intercourse but also of the ejaculation is a badge of manhood. The greater the force of the ejaculation, the greater the manhood of the ejaculator.

Such talent can be a source of braggadocio—"I pulled out and shot my load clear across the room." Even women may brag about a lover's strength of ejaculation. One woman told me: "When I jerked him off for the first time, his orgasm was so powerful, the cum stuck to the ceiling of my car. See those spots?"

In contrast to the almost mechanized aspects of macho sex, there are men to whom sex is a form of communication. It may also represent the symbolic union of the genders. They see it as the most profound way to get to know another person and to build a bridge of intimacy and affection. In a similar vein, other men find the sex act and climax inseparably melded to feelings of caring and love. Their great delight lies in giving pleasure to their partners.

How men describe the penile orgasm

"Penile waves or peaks, sometimes continuing for what seems to be minutes, but is probably 60-70 seconds, accompanied by body shudders."

"My body shakes and I go through rhythmic contractions—sometimes my hips take over, sometimes my whole body. The orgasm seems to last forever. Time has stopped and ecstasy is the dance of life. There are waves of pleasure running up and down all over my body. I am no longer present as a personality. It's all pleasure and I hear myself moan."

"It starts deep in the pelvic area. I can feel the jism moving up to my prick. Everything vibrates and I shoot off."

"Heat goes through the genital area along with extreme pleasure. The ejaculation is like a spring letting go."

Study Findings

Of all men (130), from the Primary Group participating in this research, 98% (127) reported having penile orgasms.

2. THE PROSTATE AND ANAL ORGASM

Throughout the work on the Orgasm Spectrum Research Project, the following definition of the man's anal orgasm was used: *the anal or prostate orgasm happens at the height of and/or prostate stimulation, may begin in the anal area or prostate and may expand from there.*

In November/December 1998, I began the concluding editorial work on this book. I asked a well-known, widely-published sexologist who had outstanding editorial skills to read the manuscript critically before I began the final editing process. He made numerous excellent suggestions.

The most important of these was the notation that in the woman's report of her orgasm spectrum, I had concluded that she was capable of having both a G-Spot orgasm and an anal orgasm. However, while identifying the man's orgasm spectrum, I had identified the anal and prostate orgasm as being one and the same. Since the man's prostate is analogous to the woman's G-Spot, to be consistent, I should have listed the man's prostate orgasm separately from the anal orgasm. This especially in view of the fact that the man can have an orgasm either from stimulation of only the prostate, or from stimulation of only the anal sphincter. The latter practice, when the tongue is used, is called "rimming" or "anolingus." Men are capable of having a unique climax from these two types of stimulation.

I am pleased to correct this error and again wish to thank my colleague for pointing this out. The corrected definition of the prostate orgasm would now read: *the prostate orgasm happens at the height of prostate stimulation, may begin in the prostate and may expand from there.*

For most men, any form of anal stimulation is associated with homosexuality, "sin," "dirtiness" or sodomy. There is also the powerful social conditioning which they have experienced related to toilet training and the expulsion of feces. This combination of forces erects strong psychological barriers which prevent the vast majority of men from seeking or experiencing a prostate orgasm. Healthier attitudes toward sexuality have begun to emerge. As a result, the incidence of the prostate climax by heterosexuals has been increasing. This trend can be expected to take a quantum leap in popularity when the epidemic of AIDS is finally eliminated.

Why the prostate?
Women have the G-Spot, while men have a prostate gland which can be a major source of sexual excitation. Due to its location, it is readily accessible. The gland can be felt an approximate finger's length into the anterior wall of the rectum. It lies directly below the bladder, surrounding the neck of the bladder and the urethra's upper part, and contributes secretions to the seminal fluid.

The functions of this gland lend themselves to misunderstanding. According to many medical texts, its major (and only) function is to secret certain fluids. However it has another purpose than contributing to the seminal fluid to foster conception. *The prostate gland is a major component of the male sexual nervous system and functions as a primary source of sexual excitation.* Seconds before the orgasm, the gland is the center of a number of intricate reflex responses. Immediately prior to orgasm, to prevent semen from backing up, the neck of the bladder closes and the urethral sphincter opens. (This is the sphincter that multi-orgasmic men seem to have brought under voluntary control.)

The prostate now joins other internal organs in triggering a series of rapid contractions which push the ejaculate's various components into the prostate urethra. Next, the cowper glands discharge their preseminal fluid to prepare for the ejaculation, with the prostate adding its own fluid. The ampullae now release the sperm, as the seminal vesicles add nutrients to the seminal plasma. A total of seventeen glands are involved in the orgasmic process, *with the prostate playing a key role.*

In *The G-Spot*, Ladas, Whipple and Perry make the following observation:

"Almost no mention is ever made—in scientific publications at least—of the *sexual sensitivity of the male prostate gland* . . . One cannot help but be struck by the similarity between descriptions of prostate stimulation and reports from women upon discovering their G-Spot. This is not surprising, *since both appear to be evolutionary descendants of the same tissue.*" (4) Emphasis added.

Sexologist Andrew Stanway notes the following: "The majority of men who have experienced prostate orgasms say that they are different from normally-produced ones, and that for most they are far better. The orgasm seems to engulf the entire body." (5)

Observations about the prostate orgasm

In 1947, while a graduate student at Tulane University and living in the French Quarter of New Orleans, I began to see myself as an observer of social phenomena. When invited to homosexual parties, I attended them to "watch the scene." The open sex at these parties was both fascinating and also gave me an opportunity for observation. At one particular party, I observed a homosexual man enter another man anally, and, to my surprise, the recipient of his penis promptly ejaculated without his own penis being touched in any way. At the time, I attributed the ejaculation to excitement, but many years later, after I joined the ranks of sexologists, I realized that I had witnessed a prostate orgasm. At a subsequent point in my life, I decided to train my prostate to see if I could achieve a prostate orgasm. I succeeded. (See Chapter 11, pp. 198-201).

The space between the scrotum and anus in the male is

91

called the *perineum*. A number of sexologists also refer to the perineum as "the prostate spot." *Some men are able to experience sexual arousal and orgasm (apparently from prostate stimulation) on having this spot touched or massaged.* Others do not respond.

3. THE ANAL ORGASM

It will be recalled that I had erroneously combined the male prostate and anal climaxes although they are separate orgasmic categories. Erotic sensitivity in the areas surrounding the anus are the same for men as they are for women. A small number of men reported being able to have an orgasm solely from stimulation of the anus, without involving the prostate. This is usually achieved through a practice known as rimming, the term largely used by gay men (it is also called anolingus). The tongue is usually used to intensively stimulate the area of and around the anal sphincter. The anal orgasm is defined as follows: *the anal orgasm happens at the height of stimulation of the anal sphincter, may begin with the sphincter and may expand from there.*

Although the tongue may be inserted to some extent, the prostate is not touched during this practice. In an interview with a gay professional, he commented: "I can come just from being rimmed. I prefer him not to touch my penis, nor do I. I want to concentrate my whole attention on the rimming."

During the 1998 annual meeting of the Society For The Scientific Study of Sexuality, a well-known research-oriented heterosexual sexologist, who is acquainted with my work, said, "I want you to know I have had a mind-blowing orgasm from rimming." He made this comment following my presentation about the orgasm findings from my study.

I have personally been present on two occasions when gay men had an orgasm from rimming. Several heterosexual males also revealed that they had experienced this type of orgasm. Studies of the underlying dynamics of this event will undoubtedly yield quite valuable new sex information.

Psychological factors associated with anal sex

As previously mentioned, most men associate manipulation and excitation of the anus with homosexuality—a very pervasive and powerful conditioning in Western cultures. Unfortunately, this conditioning keeps men from enjoying a dimension of sexual pleasure which their physiology has equipped them to experience. Few men are aware that the prostate is a sensory organ.

In the U. S. and other Western countries, in particular, a second conditioning factor wields its influence against the use of the rectal passage for sex. Men are aware that with advancing age, the prostate may become a source of problems. They know that many older men have prostate operations, some resulting in impotence—an unsettling possibility. However, it cannot be ruled out that in numerous cases, prostate surgery may be required because this sensory organ has become an object of neglect. Is it possible that the prostate, which is both a gland and a sensory organ, needs the attention of touch to prevent some of the pathology or dysfunction?

A third powerful negative conditioning factor is that the prostate is located in the anus. Western societies instill large elements of aversion, shame and disgust toward bodily waste and the areas associated with elimination. The feelings of repugnance which people have toward normal bodily functions is reflected in the language of the streets. "Shit!" is the most-often heard expletive. Being called an "asshole" is an insult of major proportions in this country.

This powerful conditioning also affects sexologists who then become prejudiced against the anal orgasm. To cite just one sample—the sexpert Ruth Westheimer in her latest book, Sex For Dummies, (IDG Books, 1995)—makes this comment: "The anus does have a lot of nerve endings, so anal sex can be pleasurable to both the man and the woman, though of course the woman is not going to have an orgasm from anal intercourse alone." (6)

93

The prostate and the anal orgasm have long been known to exist. Numerous references have appeared in the literature of many European and Asian countries for hundreds of years. Similarly, the fact that the prostate gland can function as an organ of sexual excitation, leading to orgasm, has been known for a long time. Large scale definitive sexological studies of this phenomena remain to be undertaken.

The three key negative associations connected with anal sex and the prostate: 1) it is homosexual, 2) it is a source of medical problems, and 3) it involves "a dirty place." All erect a very strong barrier to anal eroticism. Few men have the discipline and courage to decondition themselves from these socially-fostered attitudes and beliefs. As a result, they are unable to utilize the prostate, which is an important organ of sexual excitation. Ironically, prostitutes—who lack this type of social conditioning—have known for centuries that insertion of a finger into the male rectum, coupled with a little prostatic stroking, will greatly hasten the onset of a customer's ejaculation.

This valuable sex fact remains deeply disturbing to many, if not most, heterosexual men. It is deeply disturbing due to another final psychological factor— the more macho the male, the more he will be threatened by the idea of anal stimulation. Why? Because erotic stimulation of the prostate can lead to the discovery of the receptive, passive and feminine aspects of the male self—what Jung calls "anima" and what is known "as the woman in the man" (see Appendix, pp. 223-235). The more macho the male, the more he will wish to keep these aspects of himself from conscious awareness.

There is an obvious danger associated with using anolingus. If the anal sphincter is not totally clean, oral contact with fecal matter may take place. In this way, hepatitis or other sexually transmitted diseases may infect the tongue user.

Some men experience the insertion of a finger in their anus as an invasion or violation of their private self. As a consequence, they tend to clench their anal sphincter and it

takes repeated attempts before they relax. With a relaxed sphincter, the anus symbolically becomes the
man's vagina.

"When she first put in her finger, I resisted. I didn't
want to be penetrated. I was the penetrator! It took
several tries until I could be receptive. I was too up-
tight. There were more tries before I could enjoy it.
Now I know a little what it feels like to have a pussy."

What heterosexual men have to say about prostate and anal orgasms

"The first time we fucked, my girlfriend put her finger
up my ass just before I came. I liked it.""Anal orgasm
feels distinctly different from penile. It's somewhat
duller, less intense, less pleasurable."

"She would put Vaseline on her fingers. Then she got in
two (fingers). She touched that sensitive spot until I
came. I nearly went through the roof."

"I never felt like this before. A real wild throbbing.
We now do it once or twice a week. It's a variation
from the same old 'big O'."

Finally, it must again be mentioned that I did not
keep separate records on the orgasms achieved by prostate stimulation and those triggered by anolingus or rimming.

Study Findings

*Of all men (130), from the Primary Group participating in
this research, 26% (34) reported having prostate or anal orgasms.
(Of this group, 12 men were homosexuals.)*

4. THE BREAST ORGASM

The breast orgasm happens at the peak of stimulation of the breasts, may begin with the breasts and may expand from there. In the man's orgasmic spectrum, the breast orgasm has proven to be the most elusive. Few men currently have this climax. Male nipples remain largely undiscovered and qualify as a largely repressed erotic area.

Why the breasts?

Research has shown that the male and female sexual nervous systems are in many ways similar or analogous. This can be traced to the early stages of fetal development when the fetus has not as yet urned into a male or a female. Both genders develop from the same primal tissue. For example, what becomes the head and shaft of the penis in the male becomes the head and shaft of the clitoris in the female. As mentioned previously, the woman's G-Spot is the analog of the male prostate.

If the two sexual systems are in many ways analogous, it follows that the breast and nipples are a part of the sexual nervous system of both genders. Like women, some men state they feel a direct connection between their nipples and their genitals. According to the late sexologist James L. McCrary, "About 60% of all men experience nipple erection during the sexual response cycle." (7)

It is entirely probable that all males have a vestigial (or latent) sexual nervous system connection between the nipples and the genitals. In some men this has never been activated. In others, such a connection is clearly present. Particularly in the gay community, but also among male heterosexuals, the practice of piercing the nipples with rings seem to be on the increase among the younger generations in this country. A universal reaction is "it makes the nipples more sensitive." This may lead to an increase in male breast orgasms.

In a 1978 article, sexologist Robert Chartham estimates that 75% of males are nipple sensitive, and "at least 50% of these don't know it." He then reports his own experience with nipple stimulation leading to orgasm.

96

"I have been nipple sensitive since I was fifteen. Until a year or two ago, I could climax by stimulation of the nipples (either by my partner or myself, by rolling the nipples between finger and thumb, and especially if my partner sucked one and fingered the other) without my penis being touched. Nipple stimulation is still an important item of my foreplay, either in a shared or solitary situation." (8)

In their book, *Any Man Can*, Hartman and Fithian, advocates of the multiple male orgasm, also recommend male nipple stimulation.

"Stroke your nipples (*yes, men have nerve endings in their nipples, just as women do*) with the hand that isn't stroking your penis. The nipples will grow hard (erect). Even if you don't think you have any response there, do it. Your body will react." (9) Emphasis added.

Psychological factors associated with the male breast orgasm

For the male, the breast is strongly identified with womanhood and motherhood—the breast personifies femininity. Consequently, many men have difficulty eroticizing their own nipples and breasts. There is a fear of somehow diminishing their manhood by responding sexually to nipple stimulation like a woman.

I conducted a number of interviews with men who mentioned casually almost having a breast orgasm during adolescence when their girlfriends played with their nipples. It was not uncommon for them to call a halt to nipple stimulation when they felt an orgasm approaching. ("I made her stop. I had these weird sexual feelings—I didn't want to come that way.")

It is highly probable that many men deny themselves the pleasure of having a breast orgasm. There may be fears about premature ejaculation, or these men may simply be threatened by the newness and strangeness of a sensation which is universally thought to be the province of females. In addition, a man who encourages his female partner to stroke or suck on his nipples may fear that she will think he is a closet gay or bisexual, since "real men" not only (supposedly) don't eat quiche, but are not known to enjoy stimulation of their breasts. Younger generation heterosexual adults are more ready than members of the older generations to experiment with nipple stimulation.

How men describe the breast orgasm

Indeed, while spontaneous stimulation of male nipples by U. S. women does not appear to be a routine sex practice, in the homosexual community this practice is more common. It appears to be a routine mode of stimulation during sexual encounters. According to one forty-year-old white, gay male:

> "I had my first breast orgasm . . . thirteen years ago. I had always been very sensitive in the breasts. When it started, the whole breast section became buzzy. It lit up like electric energy. Then, I had the orgasm. . . . I can now have a breast orgasm 90% of the time."

Another gay male eventually became an advocate of breast stimulation:

> ". . . I didn't like my own nipples touched or stimulated during sex. Such touching produced 'strange' sensations which made me feel 'nervous.' Now I realize the extent to which I was blocking and repressing incredible sensations of erotic ecstasy stored in the nipples. Now I experience more erotic ecstasy in my nipples in a month than most people will know in a lifetime."

There is no difference between gay and straight men when it comes to the possession of (potentially) erogenous zones. Some years ago, I interviewed three men who, according to my notes, stated they were capable of having ejaculations by having their nipples manipulated. All three were heterosexual. In two of the instances, I was also able to interview their girlfriends who confirmed that ejaculation was achieved by nipple stimulation alone. I would hypothesize that this form of orgasm is open to most if not all males who wish to be adventurous and are able to explore it. This climax will take time to develop.

Study Findings

Of all men (130) from the Primary Group participating in this research, 6% (8) reported having breast orgasms. (Of this group, 2 men were homosexuals.)

5. THE MOUTH ORGASM

The oral or mouth orgasm happens at the peak of stimulation of the mouth, may begin in the mouth and/or throat, and may expand from there. My initial hypothesis was that the mouth orgasm would be restricted primarily to homosexuals. This proved not to be the case. Perhaps as a result of the increase in oral sex over the past twenty years, a surprising number of heterosexual men reported that they had experienced a mouth orgasm.

I also theorized that among heterosexual males, the mouth orgasm would be as infrequent as the breast orgasm. Again, this proved not to be the case. Compared to breast orgasms, heterosexual males participating in this study reported having roughly three times the number of mouth orgasms.

Why the mouth?

The mouth plays a key role in the human sexual nervous system. Nevertheless, its role in sexual arousal and fulfillment tends to be obscured because we associate the mouth primarily with eating and talking. As a result, the erogenous and sexual functions of the mouth are often ignored. Actually, the mouth is a primary erotic zone. It has the capacity of triggering its own unique orgasms.

Many heterosexual men apparently come quite close to having a mouth orgasm at some point in their sex life. During interviews, five heterosexual men mentioned almost having an

99

orgasm while kissing. For three of them this occurred when they first started dating as teenagers. One man mentioned almost having a mouth orgasm from passionate kissing after his girlfriend visited him in the hospital, where he had been confined for three weeks. Another man rejoined his girlfriend after a long trip. "We necked on her front porch and kissed and kissed. My mouth got so hot I almost came in my pants." It appears that, at such times, many men abort an oral climax. This may be due to the strangeness of the developing sequence of feelings, plus the fear of encouraging premature ejaculation.

Psychological factors associated with the mouth orgasm

A peculiar paradox exists in our beliefs about what can go into the mouth. There are myriad regulations and conventions about what is sufficiently "wholesome" to put between our lips. In short, we believe that at the oral orifice, purity shall reign.

Yet, when we kiss, we freely exchange saliva usually teeming with bacteria. During oral sex, we readily trade new sets of bacteria plus the glandular secretions of the partner. To reconcile this incongruity, we practice a type of self-delusion by not dwelling on what actually takes place. This self-delusion is analogous to taking a dog to the vet to be "put to sleep," when, in fact, the dog is being put to death.

For those men with strong religious or toilet training, the sinfulness and "dirtiness" of oral sex can provide a dimension of enjoying "forbidden fruit." For some men, this appears to add a certain intensity to the oral sex experience. Other men may psychologically regress during oral sex, and relive the gratification received when an infant is put to the breast.

"About once every three weeks, I will have a powerful suckling experience at the breast of my companion. I close my eyes and become a baby at the breast of its mother. My mind is blank and I totally concentrate on the suckling. When I am through, I feel energized and rested. She understands and likes it."

As previously mentioned, I personally observed an

instance of homosexual fellatio in which the fellator's suckling appeared to be rhythmical, like that of a baby. Subsequent conversation with the fellator confirmed this impression. In a later discussion with two orally-oriented bisexual men, I was told that they came routinely when "giving head," at the moment their partner ejaculated in their mouth—this without touching their penis.

There is nothing perverse about the gratification that results from using the mouth as a sexual instrument. Many of us have, at least once in our lives, had the urge to return to the peace and comfort of the womb. Returning to the peace and comfort of being at our mother's breast is the next best thing, and it is natural to wish to re-experience it.

For the fellator, or oral recipient, dominant psychological elements in the mouth orgasm appear to involve being receptive, submissive or dependent. Some gay men have described the fantasy of being a woman who is taking in the penis or conquering and subduing it orally. For the heterosexual male, the fantasy which encompasses being at the breast as a baby seems to dominate. Mouth orgasms in heterosexual men are usually the result of erotic play with their partner's breast and nipples.

Heterosexual men are often reluctant to talk about their mouth orgasms. As mentioned previously, this type of orgasm may be equated with premature ejaculation. In two instances of casual conversation with heterosexual men, they expressed embarassment about having a climax while orally stimulating a woman's breasts.

How men describe their mouth orgasms

"Once I get totally into it, there is nothing but my mouth and the cock. My mouth gets charged up and reaches a peak of sensitivity.
It's triggered when he comes. I see stars and shoot my load. Never touch my cock."

"Oral sex is much different from intercourse. I feel the oral excitement level is greater, which causes a different, more intensified feeling."

101

"When eating pussy, I am able to come with a minimal amount of penile stimulation."

Study Findings

Of all men (130) from the Primary Group participating in this research, 20% (26) reported having mouth orgasms. (Of this group, 2 were homosexuals.)

6. THE MENTAL ORGASM

The mental orgasm, occurs in men just as it does in women—either at the peak of external stimuli (triggered by outside input) or through sexual fantasies (inner directed), and without touching the genitals. Men report having mental orgasms much more rarely than do women. According to sexologist Wardell Pomeroy, less than one man in 3,000 can have a mental orgasm.

In the initial stages of my research on the Man's Basic Six, I believed that mental orgasms were due to "excessive sexual excitation"— perhaps coupled with unconscious self-stimulation of the genitals. Then I recalled an incident that took place when I was a senior at the University of Michigan. During an all-male gathering, at a cooperative, we talked about different forms of masturbation. At some point in the discussion, one man (who later became a highly-honored physicist) mentioned that he could come without using his hands or rubbing his penis. There was much jeering, hooting, laughter and universal disbelief. My good friend, the late Harold Lester, proposed a bet. The man who had made the claim covered all bets as he reasserted that he could climax by "mental concentration" alone.

On the day of the event, we assembled in this man's room. He took his penis out of his trousers, asked for complete quiet and closed his eyes. After a while his penis became erect. Then his breathing quickened, his face reddened slightly and there was an ejaculation. There were subdued cheers and talk as the man pocketed his winnings with a smile on his face. He was asked again how he did it. He replied that "I think of sex and concentrate."

102

It is very clear that the man, similar to the woman, is capable of having a mental orgasm. Another example from an interview with a gay participant in this study:

"I had my first orgasm to music when I was sixteen years old—to the song "What's the Matter, Baby." Della Reese delivered a very driving song. Years later a group did a song, "Baby, It's You." Again that driving rhythm—I orgasmed. There was no sexual deprivation (at these times).

"My boyfriend and I went to the opera. There is a particular spot in La Traviata where the music builds up. My body would build up and I would get a hard on and orgasm. It's not an ejaculatory one."

During my research interviews, it was my distinct impression that men tended to avoid talking or writing about their mental orgasms. In spite of repeated pleas to obtain written descriptions of this type of orgasm, there was little response from men. Women, on the other hand, readily responded and talked freely about their experiences with this type of climax.

We can speculate that this type of orgasm may not be readily accessible to the male, nor particularly appealing. Since men frequently masturbate by using external stimuli such as erotic photographs, or rely on their favorite sexual fantasies about women, it may be that they find little need to utilize the powers of the mind alone, since their penises are so handy. (No pun intended.) It is also probable that this type of mental control over their climaxes may be an ability, or a responsibility, that many men have difficulty accepting.

It has been my consistent experience that men, in general, are more rigid and defensive and less inclined to sexually experiment with their bodies than are women. Men appear to feel more insecure and easily threatened in relation to sexual matters, perhaps because of a perceived fragility of their manhood. It was my observation that the concept of fantasy-directed mental orgasms seem to threaten the male psyche to some degree.

103

How men describe their mental orgasms

"When I was a teen-ager, because of my strict religious background, I had this thing about masturbation. I had a false I.D. and used to go to porno films. I'd sit there and watch, never touching my rod. In ten minutes, just watching, I'd blow my load."

"The mentally induced orgasm is similar to but not as intense as a penile orgasm."

"A mental orgasm is a mind blower and very hard to describe. All very extreme, sometimes involves the whole body and nerve system."

Study Findings

Of all men (130) from the Primary Group participating in this research, 19% (25) reported having mental orgasms.

Most men of today continue to be convinced that they are capable only of a penile orgasm. Throughout history, a major aim of society has been to keep the woman and the man chained to the reproductive cycle. Overpopulation has increasingly begun to be recognized as a world problem. Both genders are now freed, by birth control, to discover the ecstasies of non-reproductive sex and the liberated orgasm. The male of the species appears more ready than ever before to abandon his socially conditioned belief system that he is capable of only a penile climax. Beginning early in the new century, the male will become increasingly involved in exploring and enjoying the spectrum of his liberated climaxes.

Notes

1. Mina B. Robbins and Gordon D. Jensen, "Multiple Orgasm in Males," *Journal of Sex Research*, 1 (February, 1978): 25.

2. Alan P. Brauer and Donna Brauer, *ESO—Extended Sexual Orgasm*, (Warner Books, 1983): 4.

3. William Hartman and Marilyn Fithian, *Any Man Can*, (St. Martin's Press, 1984).

4. Alice K. Ladas, Beverly Whipple, John D. Perry, *The G-Spot*, (Holt, Rhinehart, Winston, 1982): 137.

5. Andrew Stanway, *A Woman's Guide To Men And Sex*, (Caroll and Graf, 1988): 158.

6. Ruth Westheimer, *Sex For Dummies*, (IDG Books, 1995): 178.

7. James L. McCrary, *Human Sexuality*, (D. Van Nostrand, 1973): 210.

8. Robert Chartham, "Robert Chartham on Male Masturbation Techniques," *Penthouse Forum*, (April, 1978): 41.

9. William Hartman and Marilyn Fithian, op cit.: 77.

Resources

Jack Morin, *Anal Pleasure and Health*, Third Edition, 1998. Obtainable from Good Vibrations Store, 1210 Valencia Street, San Francisco, CA 94110 ($18.00).

CHAPTER 6

THE FUSION ORGASM, ZONE ORGASM, LUCID DREAM ORGASM AND MORE

The truly liberated orgasm does not include only the Woman's Basic Seven and the Man's Basic Six. There are more colors to be found in the orgasmic rainbow. In addition to the Basic Seven and Basic Six orgasms, both genders are also able to experience the *fusion orgasm* and the *zone orgasm*. This chapter also covers climaxes which occur during dreams and the lucid dream state. The child's orgasm is then discussed. Finally, the masturbation climax plus the whole body orgasm as well as other types of peak ecstasy are briefly reviewed.

THE FUSION ORGASM

The fusion orgasm has been known for more than a decade. It was mentioned by sexologists in the late seventies and early eighties. All indications are that it has been steadily gaining in popularity among women—especially among women who are quite sexually active. *The fusion orgasm occurs when two erogenous areas, each of which may be capable of producing an orgasm, receive simultaneous stimulation so that a blending, or fusion, of sensations takes place.* Only one climax is involved, but two body parts simultaneously contribute toward its peak, thereby giving the climax its unique characteristics. The fusion orgasm is also referred to by some sexologists as the "blended orgasm," but I prefer the term "fusion" because it has a more dynamic connotation.

Having a fusion orgasm is a capability of most hetero-orgasmic women and men. Poly-orgasmic people also have reported this type of climax, but it feels no different to them than any other orgasm they have. (Some poly-orgasmic women and men report the fusion orgasm as feeling more intense.) Ladas, Perry and Whipple's conclusion that most of the woman's orgasms are of the blended or fusion type (1) coincides with my own.

It would seem logical that the clitoral, G-Spot and vaginal/cervical neurological components would be involved in many, if not most of women's climaxes. In the course of my research, a number of women mentioned they were able to discriminate between these components and identify what particular one (such as the G-Spot) was predominant in a given climax. This speaks of a high order of *orgasm discrimination*, an ability which can be acquired.

During interviews, two women noted that the fusion orgasm "seems to involve more of the body," and was therefore preferred. This preference appears substantiated by a 1984 study which found that 43% of the participants declared this orgasm to be more intense than others. "Fifteen (94%) of the 16 women who had experienced blended orgasm as one of their types expressed a preference for it, while 14 (88%) of the 16 who had experienced clitoral orgasms also had experienced and expressed a preference for the blended type." (2)

My personal experience includes relationships with several women who were capable of a fusion orgasm. Two of them experienced a clitoral/anal blend, while three others enjoyed a three-part fusion—a blend of the clitoris, vagina and anus brought about by a combination of finger stimulation and vibrators. All three women claimed that the *tri-partite fusion orgasm* was far superior to any other climax in their experience. Few women appear to explore this type—possibly because of a fear of their own sexuality. There are indications that the fusion orgasm is gaining in popularity, especially among those who are highly sexually active.

How does a fusion orgasm feel?

Fusion orgasms differ markedly, since they involve different parts of the sexual nervous system. Women reporting this unique experience describe it as follows:

Clitoral/Vaginal Fusion

"It feels similar to a sensation like a minor electric shock in my recall, except complete and totally pleasurable, relaxing and I can't keep still. My movement is triggered by a need to be able to absorb this glorious head experience. Joy, away from the tension and cares of the world."

Clitoral/Breast Fusion

"With stimulation of breast and clitoris, the feelings were more intense in both places. I call it the DOUBLE WHAMMIE, the high is longer, too."

Clitora/Vaginal G-Spot Fusion

"If a finger or other object is used to stimulate the G-Spot while at the same time a vibrator or tongue is used to stimulate the clitoris, I am capable of orgasm. First a warm feeling begins to grow from my clitoris. The feeling will flow throughout my whole body. I am no longer conscious of what is going on around me. My feet begin to have a burning sensation and my stomach muscles and leg muscles spasm uncontrollably. The feelings grow until I achieve orgasm. Little by little, I come back to earth."

Clitoral/Mouth Fusion

"Mouth and clitoral at once send me to heights so high I feel like I've left earth."

Men are also capable of the fusion orgasm. The vast majority, however, are not aware that they have this potential for a different type of sexual pleasure. Their sexual belief system dictates that they are only capable of a penile climax. Men's fusion orgasms, similarly to women's are largely experienced as being stronger. Penile/anal and penile/breast orgasms are used almost exclusively.

Study Findings

Of the 130 men from the primary group only 7, (5%) of the heterosexual men reported having fusion orgasms, while all 4 bi-sexuals (3%) and all 13 homosexuals (10%) stated they experienced fusion orgasms. However, of the 205 women from the primary group, a total of 93 (45%) reported fusion orgasms.

Participants in the homosexual/lesbian special study (see Ch. 8 pp 147-150) reported about a thirty percent higher incidence of fusion orgasms as compared to heterosexuals.

THE ZONE ORGASM

The zone orgasm occurs when a sensitive spot or zone on the body of a person not usually used for erotic stimulation (such as the side of the neck, or ears) is stimulated to a peak and there is a climactic release or ejaculation. This type of climax first came to my attention during the early beginnings of the Orgasm Spectrum Research Project.

At that time, one of the participants told me that the survey questionnaire did not cover the type of orgasm she was able to have when kissed on the side of the neck. She described this orgasm—"When my neck is kissed, my whole body goes into a slight tremble and my clitoris jerks wildly. When I totally release, my body is electric."

Based on this observation, I added a question to the survey about what I came to call the "zone orgasm." Not long thereafter, the questionnaire was administered to students in a college class on human sexuality. After class, a 28-year-old man with four years of college asked to talk to me. He said he was able to orgasm when he was kissed on the neck and ears.

"I had my first neck orgasm when I was nineteen. I used to have them once every week with a specific girl whom I've known for twelve years. The orgasm takes time— there are certain ways of doing it. She starts on the lobe

110

of the ear and works down the neck. The orgasm is triggered by ear to neck sucking. My neck orgasm is much like a penile orgasm, but seems to more totally involve the whole body in a pulsating manner—I ejaculate."

Within a week of adding the zone orgasm to the Orgasmic Range survey, a 60-year-old man reported that he had a zone orgasm when kissed on the neck. Then, in my quest for more information on the zone orgasm, I encountered a French university student, a girl in her early twenties, who had come to the U. S. to perfect her English and enjoy a honeymoon with her lover. I asked them both to fill out the questionnaire and, to my surprise, discovered what appeared to be another variant of the zone orgasm. She wrote:

"When I was 13, I felt a sensation when willing to urinate and pressed on my bladder. I had no real orgasm, but I didn't know what an orgasm actually was. Then I tried to press longer until I experienced a first orgasm. To do it, I lie on a bed, on my belly, and push against the bed with my muscles. The orgasm can be made stronger by waiting, lying on my back, until I turn over and start something. While on my back I think of some erotic image or people—former lovers and cinema stars, a kind of self video. (I always think of erotic images when I have sex.)

"During the whole thing I won't touch myself nor my genitalia. This orgasm lasts a very short time—even shorter than a clitoral orgasm—and is close to pain. (A clitoral orgasm, if done by myself is further from pain—but yet still close to it.) It could not be as great if someone was in the room with me. I could not experience it at all if touched by someone else."

Another young woman also reported having her first *zone orgasm* at the same age—thirteen. (She experienced her first orgasm at age seven, while in the shower.) While she was with some friends, "This guy came over and suddenly took my index finger and put it in his mouth. The sensation was phenomenal. It went all through my body."

This same young woman also reported a zone orgasm during her first sexual relationship with a woman, after she became an adult. She related that the woman took her whole hand in her mouth and then began sucking on her fingers one at a time. "She concentrated on my little finger. A lot of it was the use of her tongue. She was gently biting the tip, near the nail. The orgasm was heavy—it was pretty emotional, like a heavy blood rush."

In 1996, when at a social occasion, I met a district attorney who was familiar with my work. He was eager to add to my research base. With some excitement, he told me:

"I have one for your book. During a recent vacation, I met a woman, and when we went to bed, she told me she could have an orgasm by having her spine stroked gently. There was one zone on the upper part of her spine, and one at the lowest part. I identified three additional sensitive zones going down the spine. I made her come againand again until I was embarrassed because I couldn't believe it. The first three orgasms were very intense—then less so. I used a very light touch."

It has been known for many decades that both men and women have certain erogenous spots other than nipples and the genitals, although this does not appear to have been researched. These sensitive zones may be located anywhere on the body. Their stimulation leads to intense sexual excitement and for some may, in fact, leads to orgasm. It is possible that many people have not, for various reasons, explored the extent to which further excitation of their sexually sensitive zones could result in climactic ecstasy. From the limited data available, it appears that more women have zone orgasms than do men. It may be that men are reluctant to focus on these non-genital erotic areas for fear of premature ejaculation.

Zone orgasms were reported by participants in this study to take place on stimulation of the following areas: *the neck, earlobes, underarm (below the hair line), side of hip, "tummy button," inside the thighs, and the toes, as well as the fingers*, as previously noted. An additional factor playing a role here, appears to be a special sensitivity to stimuli, a sensitivity with which not everyone is endowed. There are some indications that the roots of the zone orgasm may lie in specific childhood or adolescent erotic experiences. Further investigation into the genesis of the zone orgasm can be expected to yield some interesting results which would greatly add to our general understanding of the human climactic experiencing.

My research into this type of orgasm indicates that a host of other parts of the body than those identified as components of the sexual nervous system can be utilized to trigger a climax. Can this capacity be learned or acquired? Can selected parts of the body be eroticized to become a source of orgasms? Discovery of this process can be expected by the end of the first part of the 21st century.

The zone orgasm appears to be considerably more prevalent than I had initially suspected. However, interviews also revealed that relatively few women have had the experience of a lover patiently exploring all areas of the body to see if a zone orgasm is possible. The same can be said for men.

Study Findings

A total of 216 persons from the Primary Group filled out the questionnaire containing the zone orgasm item. Of this number, 31 women and 8 men stated they had experienced a zone orgasm.

DREAM ORGASMS

The dream orgasm is a widespread phenomenon, with many people experiencing dreams which are sexual in nature. Both men and women enjoy such climaxes, which begin while they are asleep, but usually serve to awaken them. The latest Kinsey Report reveals that about 40% of women have experienced orgasm during an explicit sexual dream and such dreams seem to increase with age. Men, more than women, stated that their dream orgasms were "more intense, or very intense."

Some people have dream orgasms during periods of celibacy, while others experience them as an adjunct to an active and satisfying sex life. However, those who have infrequent sex are more likely to have dream orgasms than those who have sex more often. This appears to be due to the fact that the dream climax releases pent-up sexual energy.

Dream orgasms vary in intensity—from more intense to less intense—when compared with climaxes experienced when awake. One man noted that his occasional orgasms during dreams were "less physical and direct, but warmer and more ethereal." Both men and women described their dream climaxes as *different* in quality from any other climax. The "wet dreams" of men satisfy some and irritate others. Some people report feeling somewhat anxious, either during or after such an orgasm, although orgasmic dreams are neither unusual nor unnatural.

Lucid Dream Orgasms

The concept of lucid dreaming is not new—instances of this phenomenon have been recorded throughout history. Scientist Stephen LaBerge, the foremost pioneer in research on lucid dreaming, defines it as "dreams in which you know that you are dreaming, and are aware that the dream is your own creation." In other words, lucid dreamers can control what happens during a dream, *including being able to have a climax at will.*

Dr. LaBerge is associated with Stanford University and is the founder of the Lucidity Institute (see the Resources section at the end of this chapter.) His book, *Lucid Dreaming,* remains the leading volume on this subject. Dr. LaBerge has developed a number of electronic instruments plus training programs to help people achieve lucid dreaming.

In her book, *Pathway to Ecstasy,* researcher Patricia Garfield concludes that "Orgasm is a natural part of lucid dreaming." (3) LaBerge, responding to this comment, argues that erotic lucid dreaming is neither natural or unnatural, but more likely a matter of "as the dreamer, so the dream." That is to say, it is the dreamer, not nature, who exerts control over the erotic content of his or her lucid dreams.

Dr. LaBerge cites the following five benefits of lucid dreaming:

"*Experience unparalleled adventure.* Discover the ecstasy of flying . . . enjoy complete sexual freedom, fulfill your wildest fantasies."

"*Tap creative inspiration.* Throughout history, dreams have inspired many ideas and inventions in a variety of fields."

"*Enhance your abilities.* Lucid dreams are so real that you can use them to practice and improve skills."

"*Overcome fears.* The confidence you acquire from facing dream fears can extend into your waking life, where you can use it to face and overcome fears and inhibitions that may be hampering your progress and limiting your freedom."

"*Discover transcendence and illumination.* The Tibetan Buddhists have used lucid dreaming for many centuries to help them attain realization of the illusory nature of experience. Such revelation is a signpost on the road to transcendence of ordinary being." (4)

During an interview in 1995, LaBerge added another benefit of lucid dreaming: "Lucid dreamers say they can actually recognize the symbolic meaning of their dreams while still asleep, and can therefore perform their own do-it-yourself, on-the-spot psychotherapy."

Lucid dreaming offers a unique sexual experience. Both the sexual act and orgasm *feel different.* Imaginative erotic scenarios can be acted out while dreaming, and new pleasurable sensations explored. Since we spend a great deal of time sleeping, lucid dreaming offers an unparalleled opportunity to enrich and extend the sex life. *The individual development of the lucid dream orgasm provides a particularly interesting adventure into the inner universe.*

THE CHILD'S CLIMAX

Children are certainly capable of sexual arousal and orgasm. A number of participants in the Orgasm Spectrum Research Project mentioned that they recalled having had orgasms during their early childhood. Such an orgasm is by no means rare, but is quite common among children, beginning in infancy.

The childhood orgasm has been variously described as "like a quick sting," "a little buzz," and "a drawing, intense, exquisite, almost burning sensation." A common characteristic appears to be the preceived brevity of its duration. However, in some people, this early sexual experience may be repressed or simply "forgotten." In others, it may be remembered, but disbelieved.

Children fondle their genitals as a matter of course, since this type of sex play is highly pleasurable. However, numerous parents still view this as "dirty," or "naughty," or "sinful," and are quick to admonish or punish the child. In my own experience, my father once pointed out a hunchback, and warned me that I tempted the same fate if I dared to play with my penis, as the hunchback surely had. As a result, when I first began to masturbate, I would look over my shoulder afterwards to see if the hunchback had started growing.

There is a widespread denial of the fact that children are sexual beings. Many, if not most children lead their own sub rosa sex lives from early infancy to adolescence. It is normal for children to express and explore themselves sexually. *This is a natural learning process as well as a healthy form of preparation for the future.* Unfortunately, the orthodox, conservative, repressive elements of our society promote the myth that children are "pure" and unsullied by sex in any form. These ultra-conservative elements use the "purity of a child" myth to attack sex education and explicit descriptions of sexual activity, while advocating sex censorship, thus promoting deep-rooted fears, ambivalence and guilt about sex.

One way to combat this vicious cycle of repression is through more comprehensive studies of the sex lives of children which we already know have their beginnings in infancy. Giving maximum publicity to such studies will progressively reverse the forces of ignorance and narrow-mindedness. In the new millennium, there will be a major shift toward more enlightened attitudes, perspectives and practices in the area of human sexuality. This includes acceptance of the fact that children lead their own sex lives and are sexual beings. Their needs must be respected to help them develop healthy sex lives.

THE MASTURBATION CLIMAX

Not long ago, the word "masturbation" was only mentioned in whispers. Various U. S. denominations and religious authorities continue to insist to this day that masturbation is not only harmful, but a shameful, perverted and sinful practice. According to a 1995 study of religiosity and sexuality, "Woman who frequently attend religious services were more likely to perceive masturbation as both a sin and an unhealthy practice." (5) There is no evidence whatever that masturbation causes any disorder, nor is it the result of any illness or dysfunction. Rather self-loving (a term coined by the author Betty Dodson) plays a significant role in people's sexual development and the human life cycle.

It is well known that infants persistently touch their genitals. Less well known is the fact that many infants experience orgasm. Childhood masturbation is now understood to be part of a healthy developmental sequence which parents increasingly accept. In adolescence, teen-agers use masturbation not only to release tension, but to develop an awareness of their sexual selves.

Acts of masturbation are now openly seen on day time soap opera television. For instance, the program *Mad About You,* in mid-1995, showed a woman mounting a washing machine. She had an obvious orgasm from the vibrations. In contrast, the Vatican, in December 1995, under Pope Paul II, issued a *Family Guide to Sex* which called masturbation "a grave disorder" characteristic of immaturity and for which there is no moral justification.

During interviews for the Orgasm Spectrum Research Project, a large proportion of both men and women spontaneously mentioned that masturbation resulted in the most intense climaxes. However, an equally large number found being masturbated by their partners as "more pleasurable."

Aside from instances of absence or illness of the partner, or quarrels, four major forces seem to be at work when a member of a couple masturbates.

1. During the masturbation climax and the resultant sexual energy flow, a redistribution of energy takes place in the body. Sex is basically an energy phenomenon, and *self-stimulation apparently produces a different flow and distribution of energy than does coitus.* The particular energy redistribution which takes place during self-loving is needed by the body.

2. The masturbation orgasm, the most common of all climaxes, is usually achieved rather quickly. Most individuals do not appear to use a playful or gradual build-up toward the orgasm. They do it as quickly as they can, possibly due to fears of discovery conditioned during childhood. As previously mentioned, many if not most men and women experience this as being the most intense climax.

3. Autonomy needs are also operative. A long, close relationship between two people establishes a spectrum of emotional dependencies. Such bonds need periodic "loosening" or "flexing," a reconfiguration which is facilitated by the solo climax.

118

4. Sexual habituation and the human need for variety are also at work as partners seek solo gratification. Self-loving provides a very distinct, different type of sexual experience.

THE WHOLE BODY ORGASM

It is evident from interviews conducted during this study that for the vast majority of people, the sexual pleasure associated with the climax is largely centered in the genital area. For hetero-orgasmic persons, the part of the sexual nervous system (such as the breast), called the trigger component, adds specific feelings to the climax. A minority of these individuals appear to experience a whole body orgasm (W.B.O.). For such individuals, their sexual pleasure spreads to many or all parts of the body. (This type of orgasm has been briefly mentioned in their publications by a number of sexologists.)

When the W.B.O. occurs, it is often described as a form of sexual ecstasy, or energy, which has now spread to the rest of the body, or most parts. A dissolution of the "sense of the normal self" is often described as well as feelings of bliss—"a new wholeness"—and being energized by the experience. It is routinely reported as being "distinctly superior," more satisfying, or fulfilling, than the genitally centered climax. (It may be accompanied by contractions of the whole body.)

Individuals who have experienced a shift from the genitally centered to the whole body orgasm could give no consistent reasons as to why and how this shift took place. For the most part, the comment was "it just happened." Speculations ranged from "it happened because I was deeply in love for the first time," to "I lost some of my (sexual) inhibitions just before it happened." As previously mentioned, whole body orgasms were also reported by both men and women who danced before the late Indian guru Baghwan Shree Rajneesh.

It has been my impression that since 1995, an increasing number of men and women have been experiencing the whole body orgasm. Only two instances have come to my attention where the whole body orgasm was subsequently replaced by the genital type of climax they had previously expe-

119

rienced. In both cases, hospitalization and illness were involved. Possibly intercourse was resumed before total wellness was achieved.

The universality of very positive reactions and enthusiasm about the W.B.O., as well as references to the marked post-orgasmic sense of well-being, may indicate that it functions to enhance health. It is my hypothesis that during this type of climax, the bio-electric sexual energy is distributed more generally throughout the body. The dynamics of this process and how to make the whole body orgasm universally available so that sexual energy can be consciously channeled from the genitals to the body, will undoubtedly be discovered in the new century. A research project to study the dynamics of this shift and factors associated with it is needed.

I hope to begin this work some time in the year 2000. Colleagues and individuals who are interested in shedding more light on the whole body orgasm are invited to correspond.

OTHER TYPES OF PEAK ECSTASY

Much remains to be discovered about human sexual functioning and new findings continue to be reported. For example, at the Third Asian Conference on Sexology in New Delhi, a new area of erotic sensitivity was reported to have been discovered. Dr. Chua Chee Ann, a Malaysian sexologist, reported the presence of an erotic area which he called "the anterior fornix erotic zone" or AFE.

It is a spongy area in the vagina at about the same location as the G-Spot. According to Dr. Chua: "Very gentle, light strokes to the AFE Zone, as opposed to the firm strokes of the G-Spot stimulation technique (personal communication: Whipple, 1994), have evoked erotic responses in women, which have never been mentioned before by other researchers. In this study, the AFE Zone appeared to be endogenously erotogenic in most of the women studied." (6)

When the AFE zone is stimulated, vaginal lubrication as well as orgasm is noted. Dr. Chua reported that all but eleven of 193 women in his Kuala Lumpur study reported vaginal lubrication and increased erotic pleasure, and often orgasm, from stimulation of this zone. Perhaps, similar to the G-Spot, only a certain proportion of women have this sensitive area. Or is it merely present in Asian women?

Also reported in the sexual literature of the twentieth century (and before), is the fact that for some men and women, stimulation of another spot triggers erotic pleasure and yields an orgasm. This is the so-called urethral or "U-Spot." The U-Spot orgasm, according to reports, is a different type of climax, and has its own unique characteristics, for many, if not most of those reporting it. (A major hazard here is contracting a urinary infection.) More research of the AFE Zone and U-Spot is needed.

In 1997, sexologist Barbara Keesling published a book called *Super Sexual Orgasm* (SSO). In her book she uses extensive P.C. muscle exercises in preparation for the SSO.

"The key to the super sexual orgasm lies within a small passage of the vaginal canal, just beyond the cervix, known as the cul-de-sac . . . this small section of the vaginal canal is so extraordinarily rich in sensitive nerve endings that the slightest contact with a man's penis, or sex toy, can trigger an instantaneous orgasm . . ." (7)

Keesling calls this orgasm "the cul-de-sac response." She points out that in most women, the uterus compresses the vaginal canal, creating an obstruction at the entrance to the cul-de-sac passage. This prevents entrance of the penis, or a sex toy. Her detailed P.C. exercise program is designed to make entrance to this area possible.

Finally, an interesting fact must be mentioned. The main series of interviews for this study were conducted from 1985 to 1988. However, in the years following, numerous additional interviews about the human climax were obtained. In this latter period, 15-20 women volunteered the same information.

The women mentioned that the so-called "sex sandwich" yields orgasms of an extremely high intensity, plus a spectrum of new erotic feelings. Many of these women asserted that the sex sandwich gave them the ultimate or "cosmic" orgasm. The French novelist Colette gave a detailed description of this particular sex act in one of her novels. The passage gained considerable notoriety and this sex act came to be called "sandwich á la Collette" in France. The act is also known as "double penetration." In the U. S., over the past decade, more than a dozen porno videos have been issued featuring this practice.

While using the "sex sandwich," the woman is in the middle as she invites one man to introduce his penis into her vagina. The other man introduces his penis into her anus at the same time. It would seem logical that the high sensory input by the two male bodies contributes both to the erotic sensations and the intensity of this apparently unique climax.

ADDENDUM

Some time after signing a contract with a publisher for this volume in 1988 (see Introduction) I sent a copy of the manuscript to Dr. Beverly Whipple, a leading researcher in the field of sexology. After reading the manuscript, she made a statement supporting this work. (The statement was repeatedly used to announce publication by the publisher who never issued the book.)

In November 1998, I presented a paper to the Society For The Scientific Study of Sexuality at the annual meeting in Los Angeles. I participated in a symposium entitled: "Orgasm— Recent Models and Methods." The title of my paper was "The Orgasm Spectrum Research Project." After my presentation, Dr. Whipple turned to me and said she had done research on the zone orgasm and that this research verified its existence. She gave me her bibliography and marked the two relevant articles indicating the research. They are:

1. Komisaruk, B.R. and Whipple, B. Love as a sensory stimulation: Physiological effects of its deprivation and expression. In *Psychoneuroendocrinology* (in press).

2.   Whipple, B., Gerdes, C.A., and Komisaruk, B.R. (1996). Sexual response to self-stimulation in women with complete spinal cord injury. *Journal of Sex Research,* 33(3):231-240.

Notes

1. Alice K. Ladas, Beverly Whipple and John D. Perry, *The G-Spot,* (Holt Rinehart and Winston, 1982) : 152.

2. Mary Jo Sholty, Paul H. Ephros, Michael Plaut, Susan H. Fischman, Jane F. Charnas, Carol A. Cody, "Female Orgasmic Experience: A Subjective Study," *Archives of Sexual Behavior,* 2 (1984): 159.

3. Patricia Garfield, *Pathway to Ecstasy,* (Holt, Rhinehart, Winston, 1979): 288.

4. Stephen LaBerge, *Lucid Dreaming,* (Ballantine Books, 1993): 114.

5. J. Kenneth Davidson, Carol A. Darling, and Laura Norton, "Religiosity and the Sexuality of Women," *The Journal of Sex Research,* 32C (1995): 242.

6. Chua Chee Ann, "The Reflex Induction of Vaginal Lubrication and the Enhancement of Vaginal Erotic Sensitivity in Women Using the AFE Zone Stimulation Technique." (Unpublished article).

7. Barbara Keesling, *Super Sexual Orgasm,* (HarperCollins, 1997): 5-6.

Resources

The Lucidity Institute, 2555 Park Road, Suite 2, Palo Alto, CA 94306. (1-800-GO LUCID). Their latest catalog contains information about publications, electronic devices, workshops, etc.

CHAPTER 7

THE ORGASMIC STATES OF BEING, ORGASM SHAPING AND OTHER DISCOVERIES

Knowledge about the *Orgasmic States of Being* expands self-understanding and can bring even greater brilliance and ecstasy to the orgasm. Awareness of these states of being also provides a framework for communicating about the climax, as well as aiding in the creative shaping of the orgasm, thus opening the door to new dimensions of peak erotic experiencing. Several other discoveries are discussed in this chapter. The use of *orgasm tone* adds new and unique high pleasure characteristics to the climax. The principal components of the climax are discussed in the next section. This is followed by a brief review of the major orgasm body patterns. Finally, there is the *orgasm herald,* of special interest to women.

The subjective feeling states that people experience during orgasm have, so far, received relatively little attention. This may be because the highly intimate nature of the sexual experience has discouraged people from talking about the subjective content of their climaxes. The landscape of peak ecstasy, however, is far more complex than has previously been suspected. In fact, a very large unexplored universe lies hidden within the human orgasm.

It has been a tendency among professionals to describe the orgasm in terms of a tension release. Sexologist Alfred Kinsey, for example, defined it as "the explosive discharge of neuromuscular tensions at the peak of sexual response," In her book *Eve's Secrets* (Random House, 1987), medical researcher Josephine L. Sevely concludes that during the orgasm, the man and woman experience at least three feelings:

• "A sensation of piercing compulsion . . . an awareness

that orgasm is coming ... we know we are about to cross a threshold, there is no turning back, it is inevitable.
• a sensation of erotic transport.
• a sensation of ecstasy that rushes us across the threshold, where we find ourselves and return to our normal consciousness." (1)

Sevely also did a very thorough investigation of medical history, plus laboratory analysis, of the female ejaculation. She calls it the female prostatic ejaculation. She also joins the numerous researchers who have concluded that this ejaculation is not urine but largely glandular secretions. This again refutes the Masters and Johnson erroneous doctrine about this phenomenon—that the secretions are urine or do not take place.

Among those who have done research about the psychological dimensions of the sexual experience, the work of the well known sexologist Donald Mosher (2) is particularly relevant. Mosher proposes that during sex, people experience and are able to utilize three major emotional dimensions. They are the *sexual trance state, partner engagement and role enactment.* These are independent of as well as related to the genital response and the orgasm. In each of these dimensions, a person's involvement can vary from low levels of depth to total absorption.

Finally, it must be mentioned that researchers have noted that both a *dimming* of consciousness, as well as a *sharpening* of consciousness can take place during the orgasm. It is my observation that this varies with the individual and the various components that he or she brings to the sex act.

A sexual climax is not merely an ecstatic moment, but a multi-layered event involving what I have come to call the "orgasmic states of being." By definition, the orgasmic states of being are *dominant mental states, attitudes, fantasies, images or other phenomena which prevail during the climax,* and which are present in *addition to* the unique characteristics of the orgasm itself. The orgasmic states of being co-exist with the unique characteristics of the orgasm (the trigger component attributes) which, in the hetero-orgasmic person, is determined by the source of stimulation such as the clitoris, penis, breast, etc.

Since orgasmic feelings and sensations are different every time a person makes love, becoming increasingly aware of one's orgasmic states of being provides a form of enrichment of the climactic experience. The orgasmic states of being furnish a framework, or map, to explore the riches of the vast inner universe of the human climax. The states of being can also be shaped or developed. This is discussed subsequently in the light of my own learning experience while discovering these states. Finally, by being aware of your orgasmic states of being, patterns can be identified which furnish valuable clues to self-knowledge, as well as a greater depth of understanding of the relationship in which sex takes place.

When the Orgasm Spectrum Research Project was more than half completed, I began to notice clues and statements in interviews which previously had not caught my attention. They revealed that the orgasmic experience was, for many people, much more complex than previously suspected. Following through on these clues in subsequent interviews, it was evident that, for many, the climax was a multi-layered experience which had numerous dimensions. It was also clear that for many, "all orgasms feel the same." *This latter group had overwhelmingly never directed their conscious awareness into the climactic event.*

After an initial exploratory study, the Orgasmic States of Being Survey, containing six descriptive items, was developed. A modest study involving 24 men and 24 women who filled in the survey was then undertaken. (A seventh state of being was added in the early nineties.)

THE SEVEN ORGASMIC STATES OF BEING

1. Chaotic Ecstasy
This orgasmic state of being is a mixture of very intense, highly pleasurable sensations which blot out everything else. Awareness centers on these ecstatic feelings of peak pleasure. There is no consciousness of the self.

"The highest feelings of joy and pleasure nothing else exists."

"I lose myself in the jumble of intense ecstatic peaks which I seem to be riding on, or floating on."

2. Fantasy/images

This orgasmic state of being includes specific erotic images or fantasies of sexual parts or sexual scenes which flash across the screen of the mind during the climax.

"When I come, I fantasy past lovers, new sex postures or different places to do it."

"There's this screen in my mind with erotic images when the climax hits me. It helps me to climax."

3. Body focus

This orgasmic state of being is an intense awareness of peak pleasure sensations in particular body parts (usually the genitals), or a focused awareness of ecstatic sensations taking place over the entire body.

"It begins and stays mostly in my genitals."

'I distinctly feel waves of pleasure washing all through my body and I'm aware of the contractions."

4. Intrusive thoughts

This orgasmic state of being includes a variety of intrusive or annoying thoughts which may occur during the climax and which may actually have a negative effect on the experience.

"I go on this guilt trip or think of a friend or relative when I orgasm."

"I keep remembering things I should be doing like errands or cleaning, or I try to figure out when my partner will come."

5. Multi-dimensional climactic experiencing

This orgasmic state of being includes visions, or images, of a highly aesthetic nature. These changing vistas, usually in color, may pulsate with the ecstasy of the orgasm, and a sense of timelessness is often present.

"I have these very, very intense images of the most beautiful experiences with flowers and colors I have had throughout my life. The colors are absolutely vibrant and once every six months or so I feel like I am the faint echo of Divine Laughter— a very deep spiritual experience."

"I see these magnificent panoramas from the top of a mountain, or I see fields of flowers and sunsets the colors are unbelievable."

6. Peaceful orgasmic experiencing

This orgasmic state of being incorporates harmonious, tranquil and calming feelings although, occasionally, mild anxiety about loss of control may co-exist with feelings of clearness, contentment and serenity.

"The orgasm is very calming and at the same time somewhat anxiety producing fearing loss of control and uncontrollable responses."

"Very content and serene feelings of happiness, being in harmony and calmness are strongest."

7. Spiritual or transcendental experiencing and feelings of melding into oneness.

This orgasmic state of being incorporates an experience of mystical union with God, the Divine Essence, or Life Force. It may include feelings of oneness with the partner and a total *loss of* the ego, or *self,* while this takes place.

"At the very height of the climax, my self is gone and I'm into a total unity with the Divine Light. For a split second, I'm in a tornado of bliss."

129

"I am inside the skin of my loved one."

"We both totally lose all boundaries. Egos and identities have vanished. We don'T know where one begins and the other ends. It's an exstasy of union."

The growing interest in Eastern mystical thought and training is feflected in this final item. Orgasmic states of be ing for many, if not most, people consist of *combinations of* the seven states (Chaotic Ecstasy and Body Focus, for example). These states of being are influenced by the nature of a person's relationship with their partner, their current physical condi- tion (energy, exhaustion, etc.) and with the use of any mind- altering substances such as alcohol or drugs. Although for *some* people the orgasmic states of being change, others re- port experiencing the same state(s) for lengthy periods of time. Not surprisingly, people may experience a different pattern of orgasmic states of being when the orgasm is induced by mas- turbation in contrast to coitus.

It was also a major finding that for many hetero-orgas- mic individuals, there were usually *two dimensions* of ecstatic experiencing. There was the particular orgasmic state of be- ing and/or its combinations. In addition, there was an aware- ness of the unique characteristic type of peak ecstasy associ- ated with the specific sexual nervous system component which triggered the orgasm.

A number of other interesting findings emerged from this study. For example, in addition to the seven identified orgas- mic states of being and their combinations, some people have other experiences. Orgasmic states of being vary on a highly individualistic basis. For example, one sexologist shared the following description:

(Man). "It begins as a slow building body sensation. The mind is in abeyance. The emotions focus into an almost light a phantasmagoric rainbow of bright color as the climax occurs, waves of feeling roll from *my* feet through my entire body. It convulses and physically the whole body contracts, first orgasm, within seconds a second orgasm, and then a slow, pulsating series of convulsions with the eyes tearing and sounds emanating from deep within the body as it tapers. The feeling is one of floating in a sea of love."

Sexologists Sandra Scantling and Sue Browder, in their book *Ordinary Women, Extraordinary Sex,* (Dutton, 1993), have a chapter entitled "Dissecting the Rose." (3) They cite thirty-one detailed descriptions of orgasms by their interviewees. Many of these descriptions are similar to those cited in the Orgasmic States of Being.

During the coital climax, for most men and women, Chaotic Ecstasy prevails along with other states. Body Focus and Fantasy/Images are also reported as occurring frequently. The changing nature of orgasmic states of being during the sex life of a person may indicate a number of things. For example, the change from *chaotic ecstasy to intrusive thoughts* may herald difficulties or problems in the emotional, or sex life of the individual.

But, for many, the orgasmic states of being are so much a part of the total climactic experience that they are taken for granted and remain unidentified. Or there may be only marginal consciousness of these states. "During the orgasm there is so much going on that my awareness is overwhelmed."

The richness and intensity of the climax is such that it is natural to totally surrender to it. But, as mentioned before and discussed in detail in Chapter 10, (Methods For Extending The Liberated Orgasm Spectrum, Part 1), *directive attention* can be used so that the multi-layered dimensions of the orgasm begin to emerge more and more clearly. Paradoxically, this increased awareness of the orgasmic states of being does not eliminate the capacity for total surrender to the feelings and happenings of the orgasm. For many, it serves to intensify the surrender to the flow of emotions, sensations and images.

By using the Orgasm Articulation Method (Chapter 10, pp. 192-193) over a period of time, not only will changes in the awareness of the orgasmic states of being take place. It will also be noted that repeated practice of this method will result in greater climactic intensity as well as *increasing the capacity to mold, form or shape the orgasm.* The creative development and shaping of the orgasm has thus been set in motion by use of this method.

THE DISCOVERY OF THE ORGASMIC STATES OF BEING AND ORGASM SHAPING: A LEARNING PROCESS

The steps and sequences involved in the discovery of the orgasmic states of being describe the learning process experienced by the writer. Knowing about this learning process will be of value to the reader who is *interested in shaping the climax in order to bring even greater brilliance, plus new ecstatic dimensions to this peak pleasure event.* It should be noted that it was a very gradual learning process for me. The reader can expect to pass through these states much more rapidly. Nor will the reader's orgasmic experience necessarily follow the same sequence of *steps I* went through.

Early in the beginnings of the Orgasm Spectrum Research Project, a novel idea suddenly appeared. I decided to watch or observe my own orgasms as they were happening, and to see where this would lead. *I would direct attention into the orgasm to become more fully aware of what transpired during my climaxes.*

This decision resulted in a sequence of discoveries spanning a period of about a year. It involved copious note-taking, but was always exciting in every sense of the word. During this period, I went through five phases of development and discovery.

Phase 1.

I found out right away that, during the climax, I was totally overwhelmed by the very strong, highly erotic sensations which were taking place. My ego, or sense of self, disappeared and there was only the total flow of peak pleasure.

The orgasms were of such extreme intensity and short duration that I had difficulty both recalling what had happened and talking about the climax. My notes read "there is

132

total absorption in peak pleasure while the 'I' of the self-conscious state ceases to exist and only the orgasm prevails." Subsequently, I was to call this particular orgasmic state of being "Chaotic ecstasy." I also discovered that I had spent most of my life in this type of climactic experiencing.

In order to find out more about the climax, I now forced myself to *concentrate, or direct conscious attention into what was happening during peak pleasure on an ongoing basis.* This marked the beginning of Phase Two.

Phase 2.

I now became very aware of not wanting to, or resisting directing my conscious attention into what was happening during orgasm. I had to use much will-power and noticed a "switching on and off" of my ability to pay conscious attention to what was happening during the climax.

Since I had decided to learn more about my orgasm, I persisted. There was a gradual increase in my ability to become more consciously aware of what took place during the climax. Simultaneously, there came an awareness that part of me was "observing" what was going on.

I also recalled that I had "played the observer" during intercourse for very short periods at previous times in my life. I had never liked this *observer function* and had used will-power to force myself to once more become totally absorbed in the (chaotic) flow of ecstasy. I *now came to realize that "directing conscious awareness" into the orgasmic process and using "the observer function" were different parts of the same coin. I* also realized that I could switch these two processes on and off. My decision was to continue to direct conscious awareness into what was happening during peak ecstasy to see where this would lead, and thus learn more about the climactic process.

During this phase I would sometimes also watch my companion during my orgasm. Will-power was used to stop this, as it diminished my peak pleasure. During this time, I also had the feeling that I was going through a transition and that this intermittent use of the "observer function" would be temporary. This proved to be the case.

Phase 3.

The "observer" began to fade and become absorbed or submerged in a focus on the body processes which took place during the orgasm—the breathing, body contractions, vocalizing, genital sensations, etc. My body focus *orgasm* consisted *not* of a total, highly sensitive experiencing of the flow of bodily processes during the climax. I let go of the observer function completely, once more fully flowing with what was happening. I realized that the decision *to flow with what was happening was a key decision.* Unconscious forces now determined what succession of physical processes, during the orgasm, would have the focus of my awareness.

Each awareness of a physical process would be crystal clear, intense and ecstatic. There was a "dance of awareness" as the focus shifted from one physical process to another. This dance of awareness totally varied with each orgasm. Every climax became a celebration of the body.

Next came a period where body focus and chaotic ecstasy intermingled, followed each other, or combined all during the same orgasm. I had the feeling that the psyche needed to develop or grow through each of these various processes (which I later came to call orgasmic states of being) *before reaching the readiness to move on to another stage.*

Phase 4.

A new stage did appear. This marked the beginning of my entering into what I would call *"multi-dimensional climactic experiencing."* Occasionally during the transition, the orgasmic dance of physical awareness now began to be displaced by visual color images of great richness and variety. These were fragments from the most beautiful experiences that had occurred throughout my life.

It seemed probable, at the time, that multi-dimensional climactic experiencing was associated with a mindset and/or value system which holds aesthetics in particularly high esteem. I later realized that the vast majority of people also have similar beautiful experiences in their lives. *An important factor seems to be creating or wishing to experience these very beautiful experiences again, in the context of peak pleasure.*

Closing the eyes during the climax greatly facilitates this. It was clear that the human orgasm can open the door to a very rich inner universe of aesthetic experiencing and beauty.

There was a progressive development into more and more visual scenarios of my most intense and vital aesthetic experiences (in color). These appeared to move in rhythm to the orgasm. The following is an example of such a scenario.

"There were different colors of yellow, flowers, lichens, etc. The most beautiful yellow flowers I've ever seen. All the dandelions or buttercups I smelled and loved as a child, and later, the daffodils and irises, the yellowness that is on the birches when they flower. Each yellow was very gladdening-'Wow! What a beautiful yellow flower that is, each yellow is different!' This is an ongoing delight—an ecstasy in itself. All these yellows formed flowing patterns. There was an energy flow underneath. Everything was vibrating along with the orgasm. It was a living fabric that changed and pulsated with the energy of the orgasm.

Again, it is possible to get in touch with feelings that accompanied the experience with each flower (or lichen). I sense where it occurred. There is a faint but powerful echo of the feelings associated with each flower/color/incident as the panorama unrolls. Yet, I don't want to get in touch with any particular incident. The combined echoes form a symphony of ecstasy which is too magnificent to interrupt.

While this is going on, I am once more aware that there is a bit of the critic and observer·present in me who, occasionally, watches what is happening. As soon as a part of me becomes aware of this observer, I immediately, willfully, switch back into total submerging of myself in the experience. I can turn off the observer! (I am aware that I am 'out of rhythm' at such moments.

There is a mixture of awe and humility due to being a

participant in the splendor of this orgasmic experiencing. The orgasm is both utterly serious and also ludi-
crous it— inspires laughter. In part, I am laughing at
myself for being able to let go so completely. The laughter is also an escape. if I didn't laugh, I would take the
orgasm too seriously.

By laughing about it, I can escape some of the seri-
ousness of it. On the other hand, I realize that what is
happening is totally inconsequential because the door is
going to open again and again and again to this type of
experiencing."

Once having reached the stage of multi-dimensional climactic experiencing, I would occasionally have what I subsequently termed "intrusive thoughts." These happened about
once out of every four orgasms. My intrusive thoughts centered around two areas. I would have the idea "this orgasm is
lasting so long I wonder how it is affecting my partner?" The
other recurring intrusive thought was: "Am I being too loud in
expressing my ecstatic joy?"

During this time I noticed that these multi-dimensional
climactic experiences, went through changes or stages involving different types of beautiful scenarios or images. At one
time, during a climax, I counted 26 such changing mini scenarios of flowers, etc. (It took a great deal of will-power to count
them.) This type of orgasm does not appear to be particularly
rare among those who have learned to describe what transpires during the climax. It should be clear that during multi-
dimensional and other states, there is a total flowing with
the stream of awareness, without the observer role.

Phase 5.

I now began to routinely talk about each orgasm and describe the scenarios in detail to my companion. (This in addition to taking notes.) Articulating about what has happened
was a major breakthrough. *It became increasingly clearer that
talking about what happens during the climax after it is over,
develops a sensitivity to the orgasmic process.* Most important,
it begins to foster the voluntary control, or shaping, of the

orgasmic states of being. In short, talking about what transpires during the climax afterwards, develops trust and intimacy as well as the capacity to both change and choose particular orgasmic states of being. (See also Chapter 10, pp. 192-193, The Orgasm Articulation Method.)

Once having entered multi-dimensional climactic experiencing, I noticed that on the average of about once every 6-8 months, I would have a spiritual experience.

A state of mystical or transcendental union would take place. The spiritual and transcendental orgasmic state of being is the only state which I have not been able to consciously shape or create as part of the orgasmic flow. For me, it happens only of its own accord.

During Phase Five, I realized that a number of orgasmic states of being may occur during the climax, and that *these states can be studied or observed as well as influenced, changed and developed. I* had discovered that my orgasm could be shaped. Based on interviews as well as my own experience, I also realized that the exploration of the orgasmic states of being in a playful and adventurous spirit is open to everyone who is interested.

Talking about what has taken place during the climax afterwards will, with practice, develop the capability to shape, form and develop the orgasm. *This capability can always be relinquished since the choice can be made to go with the orgasmic flow, (such as chaotic ecstasy) as it was before.* But, like learning to ride a bicycle, the ability to develop, play with, and creatively shape the climactic flow, once acquired, is always available.

When we become aware of the fact that the shaping of our orgasm is an option, or a possibility, it produces empowerment. We gain the power to create new shapes of ecstasy if we so wish. In turn, this can open to us a way of extending the range of our inner illumination.

To summarize, there are four pieces of previously largely unknown information associated with the human orgasm. First, the climax can, to a considerable extent, be developed, formed and shaped. Investing energy in this learning process brings both a greater richness, as well as intensity to the experience of peak ecstasy.

Second, the developing or shaping of the orgasm is set in motion by directing conscious attention into the climactic process as it is happening. With time, an increased awareness of what transpires develops. Third, putting what happened during peak ecstasy into words enriches and strengthens the climax. *It also makes available to conscious perception new dimensions of sensation* not previously noted during the orgasm. Sharing this awareness with a partner, deepens closeness, diminishes individual isolation and establishes a sense of oneness.Finally, talking about the orgasmic happening, over a period of time, also makes it more available to shape.

There is one more important piece of information concealed within the climax. As conscious awareness of what transpires during peak ecstasy is developed, it becomes evident that the very nature of the flow we call the orgasmic happening, or event, offers symbols and clues which can be used to deepen self-understanding and self-knowledge.

The more attention paid to symbols and clues, the more clues become accessible. A universal human tendency has been to avoid self-knowledge. However this appears to be diminishing. Becoming engaged in the quest for self-understanding requires considerable courage and tenacity.

That the orgasm can be shaped is a little known fact. Numerous people, however, have already discovered this process. They practice it occasionally and to a limited extent. A large number of these people seem not to be aware that they are shaping their orgasms, although they are nevertheless doing this. For them it is an unconscious process. Once made conscious, the flow of shaping becomes more creative and is also accelerated significantly.

The fact that the orgasm can be developed or shaped provides a challenge, especially to those who are adventurous and creative. The shaping of the climax is essentially a creative act. It involves learning a form of inner play by extending and magnifying the waves of ecstasy.

Finally, the act of shaping the orgasm brings into being new horizons and dimensions of ecstatic bliss, never previously noticed or experienced. This is a limitless universe which, in its further reaches, allows us to touch the rapture of ecstatic delight which is the Ground of All Being.

If you become interested in developing and exploring your orgasmic capacities, the following three basic principles will be of value:

• For most, the directing of consciousness into the orgasm has the effect of not only prolonging but also to some extent intensifying the climax. This is especially evident after some practice.
• Avoid introducing hierarchic judgments into your climactic experiencing such as "this orgasm is better than another."
• Always seek to become more aware of the individual nuances, feeling tones, dimensions and manifestations, i.e., the unique complex "personality," or characteristics, of each peak ecstatic event.

THE PRINCIPAL COMPONENTS OF THE CLIMAX

In previous chapters I have referred to the fact that the human climax is a complex process. This appears to be the first attempt to list the many factors, or components, involved in the event we call the orgasm.

1. The Historic Aggregate-sexual and sex-related experiences of the past, especially parental toilet training and sexual traumas, plus the nature of a person's recent sex life—all these factors may influence the nature of the orgasm.

2. Emotional Factors moods and emotions ranging from feelings of love and trust to those of fear, anxiety, guilt and shame, tension, as well as anti-pleasure attitudes, emotional involvement, etc., play a role in the orgasmic process.

3. Physiological Factors for hetero-orgasmic persons, the components of the sexual nervous system which are stimulated to climax impart a unique and characteristic feeling to the orgasm. (Trigger Component Attributes.) Optimum health,

139

as well as celibacy, recent intercourse and trauma, or disease, physical debilitation, age and fatigue also affect the climax.

4. The Time Factor-the duration of the orgasm may be experienced as being brief or longer lasting. The climactic process may also be perceived as *orgasmic infinity* i.e., as a timeless moment which appears to "last forever."

5. Orgasm Strength-the intensity or power of the orgasm may vary dramatically from low to high strength or remain about the same for a period of time. A climax having a very high intensity and other qualities (the "super orgasm") occurs rarely.

6. Partner-related Factors-the partner's activity, including movement, verbal and non-verbal communication during the orgasm can influence the nature of the climax, as can habituation and routinization of the sexual congress by one or both partners. (Also included must be emotions or moods induced by disagreements or problems with the partner, etc.)

7. Orgasm Tone-Through specific means of stimulation or devices, (for example by use of a vibrator or water jet). applied to sexual nervous system components, a climax is induced which interviewees identified as being very different from their other orgasms. Some *mono and poly-orgasmic* individuals also reported this. When playing with this concept, some of these latter individuals achieved a breakthrough and became *hetero-orgasmic.*

8. The Intercourse Belief System the meanings, values, or significance of intercourse assigned by the individual to the sex act and the orgasm can be expected to play a role in the way the climax is experienced.

9. The Bio-Electric Energy and Fluid Exchange an energy exchange on a microvoltage level takes place during coitus along with a micro-exchange of fluids or chemical components of each other's bodies. It is clear that these elements can affect both parties, or only one. The nature of these effects is, as yet, unknown and deserves intensive study.

10. Orgasmic States of Being Orgasmic States of Being are dominant mind/body states, attitudes, fantasies or other phenomena (single or in combination), which prevail during the climax. They have been described in a previous section of this chapter. For this reason only an outline is included here.

1) Chaotic ecstasy

2) Fantasy images

3) Body focus

4) Intrusive thoughts

5) Multi-dimensional climactic experiencing

6) Peaceful orgasmic experiencing

7) Peaceful transcendental experiencing feelings of melding into oneness.

ORGASM TONE—THE ADDED DIMENSION

The orgasm tone, or prevailing character, involves the awareness of a new and unique sensation, through use of a special device such as a vibrator, a penis ring or a water jet, to trigger the climax. For many persons, and especially hetero-orgasmic individuals, *use of such a special device adds a particular feeling tone which distinguishes it from all other orgasms.* The special elements which produce orgasm tone are quite varied, with each individual responding to some stimuli and not to others.

The vibrator is one of the most commonly used elements for the induction of orgasm tone. The powerful Japanese vibrators are vastly superior for inducing a deep type of vibration-this type of vibrator seems to reach inner parts of a woman's (and some men's) body, thereby eliciting novel sexual sensations. However, the penises of *some* men do not respond well to direct stimulation by some type of vibrator. Women are more likely to experience added erotic pleasure through the use of vibrators and water jets, etc.

Some women and a smaller number of men have noted that the use of these various types of devices produces a *totally different type of orgasm.* One woman put it this way: "It's very unique-you can't compare it to the in-and-out of the prick orgasm." This "very unique orgasm," in her case, was triggered by the introduction of a phallic object into the anus, to which a vibrator was applied. For this hetero orgasmic woman, this type of climax was totally different from all others she had ever experienced, including anal coitus.

For some men and women, the use of a *cock ring* (a circle of rubber or plastic which fits beneath the head of the penis) produces a unique orgasm tone. Both sexes also report the use of *anal beads* for orgasm tone stimulation. Anal beads (available in sex stores) are a series of round balls on a string which are inserted into the anus and pulled out by the partner during orgasm, thus adding a new tone.

Not all stimuli which produce orgasm tone are mechanical. Some men *report* that their orgasm feels different when they use their hands to masturbate and add lubrication. Women report a difference in the tone of the climax when a man uses differently textured *condoms,* or while using a silk *scarf* for friction on the clitoris. The following are examples of different types of orgasm tone:

"The most fantastic orgasm I ever experience is being in the spa with the water jets stimulating my clitoris and vagina. The rush is so intense, I could pass out. I forget where I am."

"I had a great thrill. My new girlfriend put large knots in a silk scarf and greased them. Then she put the whole thing in my anus. When I orgasmed, she pulled it out

THE ORGASM BODY PATTERNS

Both men and women display individual, characteristic body patterns when they climax. Three major orgasm body patterns occur during the human climax. These patterns appear to largely persist but may change during a lifetime.

Numerous men and women, at the onset and throughout their orgasm, display a certain muscular rigidity. The total body becomes rigid and the limbs are usually included. Others experience contractions of the body and limbs during the climax. The contractions follow a rhythmic sequence of body rigidity and relaxation.

Finally, there are a small number of men and women who appear to be largely relaxed during their climax. There are strong indications that, if a willful change is induced in the orgasm body pattern, this can result in an intensification of the climax. Studies of the incidence and correlates of these orgasm body patterns are needed.

THE ORGASM HERALD

In May, 1994, the writer was invited to a large wedding. On the way to this celebration, I recalled that during interviews held some years previously, a small number of women had confided a surprising fact. They knew that they were going to have an orgasm prior to its onset, because they noticed certain *body signs* which always occurred prior to their climax.

It was evident that a considerable number of young women with a college background would be present at this wedding. This seemed to be an opportunity to conduct a very limited initial study of the phenomena I subsequently called the *orgasm herald*. The question I asked wedding participants was: "Do you notice any signs or symptoms in your body, while having sex, which inform you that you are about to have an orgasm?"

A total of 26 young women, ranging in age from an estimated 20 to 36 years,. were questioned. Of this number, a surprising eight of the interviewees stated that the onset of their orgasm was heralded by tension and other feelings in their *legs or thighs* (5), with one respondent each reporting a tingling in the *chest* area, under the *tongue* and the *toes*. This very modest inquiry appears to indicate that for numerous women, the onset of their orgasm is "telegraphed," or heralded, by signs in various parts of the body. More research is needed.

143

My companion thought it was inappropriate for me to ask such questions of the wedding guests. My answer was that circulating among guests, I found that the telling of sex jokes on this occasion was a common occurrence. I believe we are now at a level of communication about sex where large numbers of people talk freely about the subject, while only hypocrites object and then tell a "dirty" joke.

Notes

1. Josephine L. Sevely, *Eve's Secrets,* (Random House, 1987): 149-150.

2. Donald L. Mosher, "Three Psychological Dimensions of Depth of Involvement in Human Sexual Response," *Journal of Sex Research,* 1 (1980): 1-42.

3. Sandra Scantling and Sue Browder, *Ordinary Women, Extraordinary Sex,* (Dutton, 1993): 45-54.

CHAPTER 8

NEW PERSPECTIVES ON SEX AND THE HUMAN CLIMAX

Profound changes in our attitudes and perspectives about the human orgasm are well under way. For example, it is increasingly recognized by people that a micro-exchange of fluids and bio-electric forces takes place at that time and/or that the orgasm can be a source for transcendental and spiritual experiencing. Most of such concepts have appeared in print, as well as on television and films.

In the first section of this chapter, *sex and the orgasm as a bio-electric energy exchange* is examined. An interesting question is raised in the next section: "Does a person's sexual lifestyle affect the range of his or her climactic experiencing?" Conclusions are based on the findings from the Orgasm Spectrum Research Project.

Several orgasm development programs, open to the public, are then reviewed. Next, a very interesting psychological process is described. It is operative every time you have an orgasm, and you may have conscious awareness of this process, or not. I have called it the *conscious orgasm power shift.* The spiritual dimensions of sex and the orgasm are then briefly reviewed. This is based on our study conducted for a book, *21st Century Sex,* of a neglected, seemingly growing U. S. trend—the spiritual sex movement. In the next to final section, the relationship of sex and the orgasm to health is explored. The final section covers a thrust which is already under way. I have called it <u>sexual self-development</u>. It is destined to become a rapidly expanding movement in the new century.

145

SEX AS A BIO-ELECTRIC ENERGY EXCHANGE

For more than four decades, it has been known by segments of the scientific community that human beings generate and are surrounded by a personal energy field. Scientists in the U. S. and Russia have measured and studied this field. It is called an "aura" by some New Age psychics and healers. The energy field is used for diagnostic as well as healing purposes by some alternative medicine and healing programs.

Every person is a bio-electric energy system, with each system having its own, unique energy configuration. Some psychics, or sensitive persons, can feel another person's energy system when in close proximity. Such sensitivity apparently can be developed with practice.

During intercourse and the orgasm, much more takes place than meets the eye. It is indisputable that a micro-exchange of fluids takes place (chemical processes) while simultaneously there is also an exchange of subtle electric energies. There is an effect on both partners as a result of this bio-electric exchange. The nature of these effects other than pregnancy remains to be discovered.

Especially during the climax as well as at the time of *mutual orgasm,* it is very likely that a more massive energy and fluid exchange takes place. In short, sex *is a chemical/ bioelectric process.* In the words of the late sex pioneer Marco Vassi, "Lovers are, for each other, the perfect conduits of sexual energy."

In their book, *Sexual Energy Ecstasy* (Bantam, 1994), David and Ellen Ramsdale pay particular attention to the sex energy concept. They point out that during sex, partners complete numerous sets of "bio-magnetic circuits." For example, numerous circuits are completed by the act of the penis entering and resting in the vagina.

Numerous sexologists and other professionals have also concluded that an energy exchange takes place between partners during the sex act. Sexologists Paul Pearsall, for example, in his book *Sexual Healing* (Crown, 1994), reviews recent research and concludes: "When we connect intimately with someone, our bodies fall into a cerebral synchronicity.

We connect on an eroto-electrical level beyond our present measurement devices." (1)

The physician Robert O. Becker is the world's foremost expert on the use of minuscule electric currents for purposes of healing. His book, *The Body Electric Electromagnetism and the Foundation of Life* (William Morrow, 1985) describes his work. Jealous peers in his field persecuted Becker. His pre-eminence is based on published research and many discoveries on the use of micro-electric currents as a growth stimulus for cells and healing. Despite this, narrow-minded administrators terminated his laboratory support grant. Beck states unequivocally that "a knowledge of the bio-electricity of growth would lead to incredible breakthroughs in medicine."

The world's foremost pioneer and designer of electronic sex toys is Dante Amore of Las Vegas, Nevada. He and his company, Paradise Electro Stimulations (PES), have designed a wide range of sex toys using low-level voltage for stimulation. Amore's creations have already received considerable publicity especially in Europe. A full length video entitled *Electro Sex,* and featuring the PES product line is available from Fantastic Pictures. It made the top ten video rental list and became the Editor's Choice for *Adult Video News. (See* Resources at the end of this chapter for PES' location.)

Early in the 21st century, the importance of the bio-electric exchange during sex will be confirmed and widely accepted. The implications of this process for people's health and well-being will be studied and clarified. People of the future can be expected to propose coitus by saying: "Let's swap some sexual energy." A number of surprising discoveries are going to result from research on the relation of bioelectric energy fields to sex. The use of sex relations and intercourse for healing purposes will be one outcome.

SEXUAL LIFESTYLES AND CLIMACTIC EXPERIENCING

A modest study of the orgasmic patterns of lesbian women and homosexual men was undertaken. This Homosexual/

Lesbian special study was consisted of a total of fifty men and fifty women who filled in the Orgasmic Range Survey. Thirty-two interviews were conducted. This appears to be the first detailed study of its kind comparing homosexual/lesbian orgasm patterns with those of heterosexuals. Since this is a small sample, the conclusions reached from this study must be viewed with caution.

The majority of the participants in this special study were comparatively young, with 78% of the men and 58% of the women under thirty-four years of age. Twenty-two percent of the men and 42% of the women were thirty-five years of age or older. The level of education was high, with 94% of the men and 64% of the women having one or more years of college, having a bachelor's degree or an advanced degree.

The study yielded evidence that homosexual/lesbian orgasmic patterns are somewhat more complex, richer and more varied than those of most heterosexuals. *Lesbian and heterosexual women differ significantly in the range of the basic seven and basic six orgasms which they report experiencing.*

There is also a dramatic difference in the number of *mono-orgasmic* (experiencing an orgasm from stimulation of one component of their sexual nervous system) women among heterosexuals and lesbians. Six times as many heterosexual women as lesbians report they are mono-orgasmic. *The anal orgasm is experienced by three times as many lesbian women as heterosexuals.* This seems to indicate that lesbians are generally more inclined to be sexually experimental, or adventurous, than heterosexual women.

There are additional dramatic differences. More than twice as many hetero-orgasmic lesbians as heterosexual women report experiencing two orgasms. *The number of poly-orgasmic lesbians experiencing two orgasms is more than four times the number of their heterosexual counterparts.*

Three distinct orgasms are cited by almost three times as many heter-orgasmic lesbians than heterosexuals, etc. It is evident that lesbian women reported experiencing a significantly higher number of all types of orgasms than heterosexual women. Is there a similar orgasmic pattern when homosexuals and heterosexual men are compared?

It was evident that significantly fewer homosexual men (38%) report being mono-orgasmic than heterosexual men (58%). *Homosexuals report twice the capacity to experience two distinct types of orgasms,* and a slightly larger capacity to experience three to five types of orgasms. The distribution of the types of orgasms experienced by homosexual and heterosexual men was surprisingly similar with the exception of the anal orgasm. Since anal intercourse is a common homosexual practice, it is not surprising that homosexual men report experiencing a significantly larger number (40%) of such climaxes as compared with heterosexuals (19%).

Fellatio is also widely practiced in male gay circles, yet only 18% report a mouth orgasm as compared to a surprising 21% of heterosexual *males. Of* the lesbian women, 24% report a mouth orgasm as do 19% of the heterosexual women. Of the homosexual men, 8% report a breast orgasm as compared to 5% of the heterosexual men. The relatively small numbers of homosexuals experiencing such orgasm was unexpected. (This may be due to the limited sample.)

A sexologist colleague of my acquaintance, on being apprised of the results of the Homosexual/Lesbian Special Study, made this dismissive comment: "People who are under social pressure about their sexual lifestyle prevaricate more about their sexual prowess than others." This simplistic statement does not refute the facts.

The dynamics of why lesbians and homosexuals report markedly different patterns of orgasms from the Basic Seven and Basic Six, can be sought in the style and type of sexual interactions which take place between same sex adults, plus the emotional components and meanings of the interaction. Also, intimate knowledge of the sexual responses of one's own body seems to facilitate sexual stimulation of same sex partners. Additionally, same sex partners appear to be more experimental and less bound by sexual conventions.

Perhaps the onus of societal disapproval vis-a-vis the homosexual/lesbian lifestyle also enables participants to pursue sexual needs and desires more freely and with fewer inhibitions. The realization that homosexual/lesbian sex is "anti-establishment" and "anti-authority" in nature, as well as being "forbidden," may contribute certain elements of freedom from the bonds of conventional sexual behavior, while adding a certain intensity to the enjoyment of sexual congress. Finally, sex appears to play a more conscious central role in the self-definition and mode of existence of the gay person as compared to the heterosexual. It is therefore not surprising that this combination of forces has lead to a greater actualization of sexual potential in those who do not follow established modes of sexual behavior.

Beginning in the late sixties and again, early nineties, there have been clear signs of a growing interest in bisexuality on the part of many U. S. citizens. Swingers' magazines have shown a marked increase in ads by individuals stating they were "bisexually curious." Several definitive books on bisexuality have been published in the nineties and a national bi-sexual organization is under way. (See Resources p. 165). Research about bi-sexual orgasm patterns is needed.

It was again evident that males in general, whether hetero- or homosexual, lag considerably behind females in the exercise and development of their sexual powers. This special study once more indicates that the woman is more sexually courageous, adventurous and experimental than the male. Women have much to teach men in the area of sex and the orgasm if men could listen.

THE ORGASM DEVELOPMENT PROGRAMS

There has been a rapid growth in the transcendent or spiritual sex programs currently available in the U. S. and abroad. Most of these programs offer sex training from a particular theological perspective such as Taoist, Buddhist, etc. Most such programs also identify one or more very distinctive types of climactic experiences which can be acquired through training. *This is further proof* that the human orgasm is <u>developmental</u> in nature and <u>can be shaped</u>. The types of orgasms acquired through training by the spiritual sex programs will be discussed in greater detail in the next, final section of this chapter.

In addition to spiritual sex training, two major orgasm development programs are currently offered: the ESO Ecstasy program and the Liberated Orgasm training. Each of these programs *focuses on* orgasm development using different approaches, methods and techniques. The oldest established orgasm development program, the ESO Ecstasy program, was developed by psychiatrist Alan P. Brauer and his wife, Donna Brauer, in the early eighties. It is based on the Brauers' experience with over 5,000 couples. A major aim of their program is to extend the *length* of the human climax.

"With continued practice, it (the emission phase) can be extended to many seconds, a minute, many minutes, *even thirty minutes or more.*
... The key to the male extended orgasm involves having the man stay as close as possible to the point of ejaculatory inevitability-keeping him in emission phase orgasm without allowing him to crest and ejaculate. This is accomplished by creating multiple non-ejaculatory *peaks. When a man experiences fifteen of more of these peaks in close succession, they may become blended into a continuous emission-phase orgasm."* (2) Emphasis added.

The Brauers' program, offered as a workshop, neglects the distinct characteristic nuances of the various types of orgasmic experienced (discussed in Chapters 2 through 7) of which both genders are capable. However the Brauers' training appears to be effective in improving intimate relationships, as well as increasing and lengthening orgasmic pleasure. There are also several sex books currently on the market which promise the reader "hourlong orgasms." On reading these books, it is clear that my own studies contradict these assertions.

The second major orgasm development program is the writer's Liberated Orgasm Training. This program:

1. Provides an overview of the major means and methods designed to bring a significant increase in erotic pleasure and peak ecstasy.

151

2. Helps participants to identify which aspects of their sexual power they wish to develop, and assists them in creating individual programs designed to actualize this potential.

3. Provides a focus on expanding sex communication as well as bringing deeper intimacy and love to the relationship.

4. Assists participants in experiencing the liberated orgasm spectrum, (with eight training methods available).

5. Also introduced is the Sex Life Development Plan, a framework *for continuing life-long sexual growth* which is based on the fact that we are using less than 5% of our sexual capacities.

Inquiries about the Liberated Orgasm Training seminars should be addressed to the author, P. O. Box 524, Silverado, CA 92676-0524.)

THE CONSCIOUS ORGASM POWER SHIFT

Whenever you have a climax, the *conscious orgasm power shift* may, or may not, take place. Acquiring knowledge about this process places you in a decidedly advantageous position. You have the option of consciously utilizing the orgasm power shift to expand self-awareness and understanding and/or to enhance and enrich peak pleasure by using this process during sex.

The conscious orgasm power shift is a subjective, or psychological, self-directed process which occurs during intercourse. When an individual focuses awareness or attention into the process we call a climax, often a surprising discovery will be made. It is the realization that *every person has an option, or choice, about the triggering of the climax.*

In using the orgasm power shift, everyone has three options. The first option is *to retain control, or power, over the onrushing climactic event by saying to oneself "I am in control of my orgasm and I will let it happen."* The second option is to *relinquish control, or power to the partner.* This is done by saying to yourself, "I am letting you trigger my orgasm and letting you make it happen." When exercising this option, issues of trust, relinquishing of control etc. are involved.

You may, of course, also disregard the two options and proceed as you do usually, i.e., spontaneously. If you choose the latter course, unconscious needs and processes usually determine what takes place during the climax. However, since you now know that a power shift can take place, a final, third, option remains. Following the spontaneous climax, you can use recall *to become aware of the process that actually took place during the climax you just experienced.* This can expand your mind/body awareness and add to your self-understanding. In turn, increased mind/body awareness expands body sensations.

Finally, it must again be mentioned that *being aware of one's capacity to effect a conscious orgasm power shift can easily be nullified by just "going with the flow," i.e., letting the orgasmic event run its usual spontaneous course.*

THE ORGASM AS A SOURCE OF HEALTH

There is increasing evidence that sex and the orgasm not only delights it heals. Several major Russian studies, completed in the early eighties, yielded some very interesting findings on the relationship between sex and health. (One study involved 20,000 people over the age of sixty.)

Dr. Semyon Dalahashvili, the chairman of the Soviet Commission for the Study of Longevity, summarized some of the conclusions from this research: "We have determined that regular sexual activity is essential to good health and long life. Being sexually active can definitely increase your life span." According to Dr. Dalakashvili, "Prolonged abstinence is clearly linked to life-threatening disease."

Summarizing another study, Dr. S. Gogokhia, head of a Soviet state gerontological laboratory concluded that, "Both men and women will live longer if they are sexually active." Other results from these Soviet studies suggest that sexual abstinence for more than one month can cause serious health problems, and that possibly eight to ten years can be added to one's life by remaining sexually active past age sixty. We are reminded of the old saying: "An orgasm a day keeps the doctor away."

Other professionals have discovered that lack of a good sex life is a major contributing factor in the onset of life-threatening illness. According to sexologist Paul Pearsall:

> "A recent survey showed that 65 of 100 women who were treated for heart disease reported feeling sexual dissatisfaction before hospitalization. A study of 131 men found that two thirds said they were having significant sexual problems before their heart attacks. Psychiatrist Alexander Lowen states, 'A lack of sexual activity should be considered for further study as a possible risk factor in heart disease'." (3)

A Swedish research project which released its findings in 1986, concludes that: "Elderly people who are sexually active have more vitality and better memories than their celibate counterparts." These researchers further concluded that *psychological, rather than biological problems are the main reason that middle-aged and elderly people give up sex.*

Specialists in aging are now agreed that barring disease-many, if not most bodily powers decline very slowly if they are properly maintained. Proper maintenance includes a good diet, daily exercise, brain stimulation, social support and a good sex life, preferably with a loving companion. The pioneering sexologist David M. Schnarch surprisingly concluded: *"Most people never come close to their sexual potential, and those who do, generally do not accomplish this until the fifth and sixth decade of life." (4)*

The relationship between sex and health is succinctly summarized by Dr. Ted McIlvenna, president of the Institute for the Advanced Study of Human Sexuality in San Francisco: "Sex is perhaps the best preventive and healing medicine there is." Dr. McIlvenna is currently researching the link between sex and health. Preliminary studies indicate that sex and the orgasm can bolster the immune system, relieve pain, help regulate hormones and can be valuable therapy for psychological problems.

SPIRITUAL DIMENSIONS OF SEX
AND THE ORGASM

There has long been an expanding interest in transcendent or spiritual sex in this country. Beginning with the sixties and into the latter seventies and the early eighties, this interest in spiritual sex has accelerated considerably, with about eight dozen or more books published since that time. There is also a magazine: *Magical Blend A Transformative Journal.* This movement may be in a cycle of its development where it is undergoing some contraction.

Much of the growing interest in spiritual sex has become associated with the so-called New Age movement. The burgeoning curiosity about spiritual sex played a major role in the "sexual, revolution" of the sixties and early seventies. Many of the young people of that period were attracted by Buddhist, Taoist and Tibetan writings and theories. Such terms as "enlightenment" and "karma" became household words.

This desire to learn about Eastern philosophies and religions was fueled by two forces. During the so-called "sexual revolution," a strong search for spiritual knowledge emerged. Inseparable from this was a powerful rebellion against the overwhelmingly sex-negative orientation of the Christian denominations of that time. There was widespread clerical disapproval of sexual pleasure and many sex practices such as "giving head"-relatively common today, were labeled "perversions."

In contrast, sex is much more taken for granted in many Eastern countries. Guilt and the concept of sin are not associated with sex. Intercourse is a celebratory event in the flow of life and offers people a path of communion with the divine. *The younger generations' of the sixties acquaintance with Eastern perspectives has helped to bring changes in values, feelings and attitudes about sex in the West.*

The cultural climate in this country has historically supported the individual's spiritual search. There is a long tradition of acceptance and even encouragement of the spiritual quest as a part of the U. S. constitutional right to religious freedom. The contemporary spiritual sex movement combines two powerful forces: the quest for sexual as well as spiritual freedom. These forces provide a dynamic impetus to a movement which appears to be only in its beginnings.

The spiritual sex movement has deep roots in human history, which roots are admirably traced in three books, including Georg Feuerstein's perceptive *Sacred Sexuality—Living the Vision of the Erotic Spirit,* (Tarcher, 1992) In addition there is Louis Meldman's *Mystical Sex Love, Ecstasy and the Mystical Experience* (Harbinger House, 1990). The scholarly *Metaphysics of Sex* by Julius Evola (Inner Traditions, 1983) is in a class by itself.

These books provide a broad basis for an understanding of the type of sex which combines erotic pleasure with a spiritual quest. From them we learn that peak ecstasy can be the key to an experience of transcendence or of mystical union. As mentioned earlier, it is a fact that *most of the Eastern sacred sex programs (such as Taoist, Tantric, etc.) provide training which expands the capacities for experiencing emotions and erotic sensations. This training also enables practitioners to have a number of new, characteristic climaxes associated with the specific program.*

Those interested in exploring the transcendent or spiritual dimensions of sexual union will make a number of discoveries. They include:

a) different approaches to sex play prior to intercourse

b) new sex positions

c) numerous new sexual techniques

d) a different perspective of human sexuality and the sex experience

e) exposure to new aesthetic elements associated with sex

f) instructions for transforming intercourse into a means of spiritual transcendence and mystical union

For women, especially, one of the swiftest ways to achieve the ability to be multi-orgasmic, or hetero-orgasmic, is probably through transcendent and spiritual sex. Elements of fear, shame and guilt are minimized if not eliminated, while the highly structured nature of spiritual sex training programs provides considerable security.

Eastern and some Western spiritual sex training programs are offered in most U. S. states and are well attended. Two of the current major programs on Eastern spiritual sex are the Indian Tantric and the Chinese Taoist. These programs and publications in their variety and scope, far surpass those offered in any other place in the world. *At this time, the United States is the headquarters for leaders and pioneers in the spiritual sex movement.*

Most of the Eastern spiritual sex training programs also help students expand their capacity for sexual experiencing, by acquiring one or more new, distinct types of orgasms. Based on the number of trainers and practitioners, Tantric sex currently seems to play a dominant role in the United States spiritual sex movement.

A variety of Tantric schools, texts, masters and sects exist, including Hindu, Buddhist, and Tibetan schools. This ancient Eastern system of spiritual enlightenment had its beginnings about 5,000 B. C. According to scholars, approximately a hundred ancient Tantric texts have survived.

Each school has an elaborate series of rituals, mantras, traditional disciplines, sex positions and training sequences which involve a symbolic re-enaction of the cosmic fact of Oneness. In Hindu Tantric practice, the male Hindu practitioner ejects his sperm. In Buddhist Tantric practice, the male practitioner retains his. In Tantric practices the man becomes Shiva-the Divine Will, or First Logos, which manifests in the creative union with Shakti. The woman becomes Shakti, the consort of Shiva. She embodies the fundamental secret forces that control the universe.

The bliss of divine union is achieved by the Tantric who joins himself to the line of force emitted in an unending stream from Shiva, the Supreme Absolute. There are many interpretations of this union. The Tantric sexpert Margo Anand's book, *The Art of Sexual Ecstasy,* (Tarcher, 1989), is one of the more clearly written contemporary manuals. Four chapters in Anand's book are devoted to the development of the orgasm. Many authorities on Tantric sex describe the Valley orgasm. Anand, for example, divides this orgasm into two separate levels. (5)

The focus of Tantra is not on the transformation of sex, but on the use of sexual energy to develop and create a spiritual experience. Tantric sex uses traditional rituals and specific sex positions to help practitioners achieve mystical union. Tantra's practitioners believe in combining relaxation with high states of sexual excitement. Sexual energy is recirculated for an extended time. As a result, there are sometimes long-lasting orgasms which are not genitally focused.

The exchange of sexual secretions between the man and the woman plays an important role in this process. Three distinct types of sexual secretions, or elixirs, are produced by the woman. They are from the breasts, mouth and yoni (vagina). Absorption by the man of these elixirs is said to nurture him spiritually. It compensates him for the loss of semen which he gives to the woman.

The Taoist program is the second largest spiritual sex program in the United States. Although other masters offer training, the Thai-born Taoist Master Mantak Chia's work dominates the scene. M. Chia heads the Healing Tao Center in Huntington, New York. It has branches in more than twenty-three states, Canada, five European countries, Australia, etc.

Lao Tzu, the founder of Taoism, lived in the sixteenth century, B. C. The opening verse in chapter 28, of Lao Tzu's work, states "To know the male/but to abide by the female . . ." Despite this admonition, of the numerous surviving ancient Taoist works, only the *Tao Te Ching* emphasizes the feminine principle.

Taoism emphasizes cultivation of the divine, inner life force, or *chi.* To live in balance, an exchange, or sharing of the feminine Yin and masculine yang energy takes place as an integral part of Taoist sex. Taoist teachings usually urge the man to control and conserve the seminal emission.

Master Mantak Chia advocates control of the ejaculation and a different version of the Valley orgasm. In the words of Mantak Chia:

"Taoists advocate the Valley Orgasm: continued rolling expansion of the orgasm throughout the whole body. The Valley Orgasm is not a technique, but rather a certain kind of experience that the lovers allow to happen to themselves.

It is a state of prolonged orgasm that generally occurs during the plateau phase when the yin and yang energies come into an exquisitely delicate balance. It is a fusion of opposites, a meltdown ... The lovers simultaneously experience an 'opening' of an energy center during a Valley Orgasm. This releases a tremendous energy that is truly thrilling as it radiates out to fill every cell of your body and joins it to follow with your lover." (6)

Taoist intercourse, in addition to the conscious exchange of yin and yang energies, involves two other major factors. They are the use of controlled harmonized breathing and methods such as the repeating of nine shallow and one deep thrust of the penis by the man. Mantak Chia's program is a total, integrated program with a strong focus on the generation of sex energy and health enhancement. It emphasizes exercises such as the Anal Pump Squeeze, massaging the prostate gland, Testicle Grip and Squeeze, and Tongue Kung Fu.

As previously mentioned, there exist numerous spiritual sex programs which teach enrollees how to have different types of orgasms. *This is another clear proof that the human climax can be developed or shaped.*

Four major Western spiritual sex programs are currently under way and need to be mentioned. They are the Judeo-Christian, the New Age Sex Programs, the Sex Magick and the Native American movements. Among the better known American Indian spiritual sex training programs are two. One is taught by Harley Swift Deer, Nagual

Elder and Medicine Chief of the Deer Tribe Metis Medicine Society. He teaches the Firebreath Orgasm, a technique which uses breathing exercises to achieve a prolonged orgiastic state. No genital stimulation of any kind is used. (See Resources).

Firebreath Orgasm training is also offered by Ms. Stephanie Rainbow Lightning Elk. A Fire Medicine Woman, she is co-founder and Cocoon Chief of the Butterfly Clan Metis Medicine Way Lodges. (See Resources at the end of this chapter.)

Most of these programs, and particularly the Judeo-Christian ones, are in their beginning stages but appear to be growing. Considerable innovation and change in the programs can be expected within the next few years. As sexologist David Schnarch so aptly expressed it: "Sexuality is a quintessential boundary experience in which spiritual transcendence and God await."

Sexologist Jack Morin, in his book *The Erotic Mind* (HarperCollins, 1995), succinctly summarizes why peak erotic experiences are perfectly suited to spiritual experiencing and transcendence: " . . . they engage us totally, enlarge our sense of self by connecting us with another or with normally hidden dimensions of ourselves or both, and expand our perceptions and consciousness." (7)

Sexologist Gina Ogden published an article entitled "Sex and Spirit-The Healing Connection," in the January/February 1999 issue of *New Age Magazine.* This is the first recent major study of American attitudes about spirituality and sex. Of the 1300 responses tabulated, 78% were from women, 21% from men and 1% from transgendered participants.

The population on which this study is based is a special one. Participants are significantly younger than the general U. S. population, more highly educated and subscribe to a belief system generally described as "new age." Ogden discovered that 82% agreed with the statement: "Sex is much more than intercourse." She also found that, " . . . almost 90 percent agree that sex contains a mystical element. Three quarters perceive sex as 'most often spiritual' with a spouse or committed partner as opposed to a casual partner." (8)

It is clear that using a spiritual approach and discipline can result in a very vast, possibly infinite expansion of the orgasmic spectrum of experiencing. Georg Feuerstein's book, *Enlightened Sexuality-Essays on Body-Positive Spirituality (The* Crossing Press, 1994), is an excellent source for this approach. The future will see a rapid expansion in the use of climactic ecstasy as a means of sexual/spiritual exploration.

SEXUAL SELF-DEVELOPMENT

In our book *21st Century Sex-The Breakthroughs of To-morrow,* we discuss a phenomenon which is widespread in this as well as other countries. We call it sexploration. An ever-increasing number of people, (many of whom have had access to sex education or to sex books) are currently exploring different ways of having sex. The very next step and almost inseparable from sexploration-is sexual self-development.

Sexual self-development is solidly based on the concept of the human potential. In the sixties and seventies, many behavioral scientists had reached the conclusion that we were functioning at less than 10% of our potential. In the area of sexual potential, the figure is probably closer to less than 5%. This is due to the fact that the ruling elites, throughout human history, have used sexual taboos, guilt, restrictive sex codes and the prohibition of various types of sexual behavior as a means to control the people.

Contemporary governments are continuing to use such stratagems. This despite a general public awareness that very little of today's sex is for purposes of procreation. Today's sex is almost exclusively for bonding and the generation of intimacy, affection and love between people, or simply for enjoyment. However sex education, in the broadest sense of the term, has become the Trojan Horse to conquer the bastions of authoritarian sex control and its ally, Puritan sexual conservatism.

In the U. S. in particular, a high value is now placed on the *liberated bedroom.* People have strong convictions that the government has no right to interfere with what takes place between consenting adults in the privacy of the bedroom.

Sexperimentation and sexual self-development today play a key role in the freedom of the bedroom.

As has been previously noted, the capacities and sexual powers of the man and the woman have been vastly underestimated. The human sexual potential is only beginning to be understood. There is a huge reservoir for intense erotic experiencing latent within everyone which can be tapped by anyone interested.

The tapping of this reservoir generates vitality and the blossoming of the life force. In short, actualizing the human sexual potential, through sexual self-development, fosters health.

Three steps are involved in sexual self-development. It begins with the recognition by a person that there are erotic and sexual capacities, energies and powers which are latent within everyone, and specifically within oneself. Next, there is a clear realization that the development of this sexual potential is worthwhile and needs to be pursued, since it fosters well-being and intensifies the enjoyment of life.

Finally, action is taken designed to broaden and extend the range of erotic and sexual experiencing (see Chapters 10 and 11). Very often, there is also an awareness that this type of self-development is going to be an ongoing, lifelong adventure. This, because the human potential for erotic sexual experiencing and sexual self-development verges on the infinite.

Why will sexual self-development become an increasingly important movement in the new century?

- You have more pleasure.
- It promotes health.
- It fosters and nourishes intuition and strengthens this capacity.
- Peak ecstasy builds up more easily, at the same time intensifying and lengthening the climax.
- Your lover enjoys more and develops increased sexual vitality.
- Curiosity and especially erotic curiosity is encouraged to grow.

- Sexual self-development fights sexual habituation so widespread among long-term couples, and introduces variety to enrich the sex life.
- It is one of the surest methods to help couples merge into the deepest form of intimacy.

Finally, it must again be mentioned that numerous restrictive religious doctrines which have repressed the American libido for generations are in the process of disappearing. The sexual belief system is no longer strongly dominated and handicapped by the notions of "sin" and "guilt." This shift favors the rapidly expanding growth of sexual self-development.

When we take a global look at sex research and the numerous sex books which continue to be published, an interesting question is raised: "What is the main purpose of all this activity in the area of human sexuality?" Our answer is: "To help people with their sexual self-development." (There has been a consensus among sexologists, for some time, that *sex is largely a learned activity*.)

The preceding leads to another question: "What is the underlying purpose of sexual self-development?" It is my answer that this process develops good sex, and good sex, in turn, nurtures and creates increased caring and loving of oneself and others. Good sex also enhances the production of life energy and *joie de vivre*.

We need all the love we can generate to save this planet, which is being ruthlessly exploited and destroyed by rapacious greed. Only more love for ourselves, for each other, and for the living entity we call Earth, will keep the human species from self-destruction.

Notes

1. Paul Pearsall, *Sexual Healing,* (Crown Publishers, 1994): 147.

2. Alan P. Brauer and Donna J. Brauer, *The ESO Ecstasy Program,* (Warner Books, 1990): 111-112.

3. Paul Pearsall, Op cit.

4. David M. Schnarch, *Constructing the Sexual Crucible,* (W. W. Norton, 1992) : 87.

5. Margo Anand, *The Art of Sexual Ecstasy,* (Tarcher, 1989) :5, 375-380.

6. Mantak Chia and Michael Winn, *Taoist Secrets of Love Cultivating Male Sexual Ecstasy,* (Aurora Press, 1984): 144.

7. Jack Morin, *The Erotic Mind,* (HarperCollins, 1995): 339.

8. Gina Ogden, "Sex and Spirit, The Healing Connection," *New Age Magazine,* (Jan/Feb 1999): 78-79.

Resources

1. Mantak Chia's and Maneewan Chia, *Cultivating Female Sexual Energy,* (1986, $12.95) and Mantak Chia and Michael Winn, *Cultivating Male Sexual Energy* (1985, $12.95). Both are available from Healing Tao Center, PO Box 1194, Huntington, NY 11743.

2. Harley Swift Deer, Nagual Elder and Medicine Chief of the Deer Tribe Metis Medicine Society, P. O. Box 12397, Scotsdale, AZ, 85267. Phone (602-443-3851.) Fax: (602) 998-2569.

3. Fire Medicine Woman (of Chuluaqui-Quodoushka traditions), Stephanie Rainbow Lightning Elk. Butterfly Clan Metis Medicine Lodge, 105 North First Avenue, #209, Sandpoint, Idaho, 83864. Phone: (208) 255-7304.

4. Paradise Electro Stimulations, 1509 W. Oakey Blvd., Las Vegas, Nevada, 89102. Fax: (702) 474-4088. World Wide Web Page: http://www.peselectro.com

5. Robyn Ochs, editor, *Bisexual Resources Guide 2000* (1999), Bisexual Resource Center, P.O. Box 400639, Cambridge, MA 02140 ($12.95)

6. *Loving More Magazine,* P.O. Box 4358, Boulder, CO 80306-4358. Single issue $6, yearly subscription/membership $30. The magazine both publishes and distributes books on polyamory.

Addendum

It appears that currently one of the most rapidly growing movements, in the U.S. is *Polyamory.* which has its own magazine (see Resources), plus multiple organizations and books. Deborah M. Anapol, Ph.D., in her definitive book *Polyamory— The New Love Without Limits,* (Internet Resource Center, P.O. Box 4322, San Rafael, CA 94913-4322, $16) has the following definition:

"Polyamory A lovestyle which arises from the understanding that love cannot be forced to flow, or not to flow, in any particular direction. Polyamory emphasizes consciously choosing how many partners one wishes to engage with rather than accepting social norms which dictate loving only one person at a time. This is an umbrella term which includes open marriage, group marriage, expanded family, and intimate networks. It could also include intentional monogamy."

In the introduction to Chapter Three of this book D. Anapol quotes author Marianne Williamson—"Our thinking that monogamy is inherently a nobler arrangement than any other has created a nation of hypocrites—which is what we've become."

CHAPTER 9

ORGASM INTENSIFICATION-
A NEGLECTED ART

As has been mentioned, the human climax appears to be an *unalterable block* of extreme pleasure which runs its course, seemingly beyond the individual's control. However, the monolithic appearance of the orgasm is, to a considerable extent, *the result of the individual's belief system,* plus conditioning and habituation.

This erroneous belief system can be overturned by becoming consciously aware of how the orgasm can be *intensified,* thus yielding an experience far surpassing one's expectations. One of the major values of climax intensification is that it represents another means to liberate and shape the orgasm. The use of orgasm intensification demolishes the conditioning and myth that "an orgasm happens and you can't do anything to influence it." A number of mono and poly-orgasmic individuals have become hetero-orgasmic as a result of using various means of orgasm intensification.

For some years, I have been in the habit of collecting and testing ways of intensifying the orgasm. My question, addressed to many people, was: "What, specifically, do you do to intensify your orgasms?" One result of this survey was the very clear impression that *most people pursue orgasm intensification in a very haphazard and occasional manner with the large majority not aware that orgasms can be consciously intensified or amplified.*

While beginning to analyze the material for this chapter, I reviewed an article by Sholty, Ephros, et al, published in the *Archives of Sexual Behavior. (1)* It contained a table entitled "Conscious Actions To Facilitate Own Orgasm." With some modifications, this table provided an excellent base line for the organization of the Fundamental Seven Ways. I am indebted to these researchers.

This is the first, most extensive collection of ways to intensify the climax. *Orgasm intensification, however, is a highly individualistic matter.* This means that certain ways described here may not work well for one person, but will yield superb results for another.

In view of the highly personal nature of the process of orgasm intensification, partners usually have to take turns trying out different ways to obtain the desired results. To facilitate this process, completely open and honest communication between partners is essential. Both partners need to be aware that they are beginning an adventure which not only can increase sexual ecstasy, but can also improve sexual sensitivity and the level of sexual experiencing.

On reviewing the Fundamental Seven described subsequently, it will become apparent that a number of these practices are routinely used by numerous couples. However, there is also a large group of people who rarely, if ever, consciously utilize any means to intensify their climax. Both groups will be interested in the two following sections which contain a total of twenty-three ways.

THE FUNDAMENTAL SEVEN WAYS

1. Getting into the "right" position

The "right" position for both the man and the woman is the one which he or she knows will yield *maximum pleasure* and is likely to enhance the orgasm. The right position for the woman may not be the right position for the man, and vice versa. Some experimentation is usually needed. One way to explore position options is to acquire or borrow a book on the subject from a local library. Videos and inexpensive illustrated paperbacks on the wide variety and range of sex positions are also available in "adult" stores.

2. Obtaining optimum stimulation

Sometimes finding the right position for intercourse provides maximum stimulation in and of itself. More often than not, however, couples discover that optimum stimulation can involve a variety of means in addition to the positioning of their bodies.

Stimulation of the various erogenous zones, prior to intercourse can be accomplished either manually, or orally, or mechanically, with a vibrator, for example. Kissing, stroking, biting as well as erotically massaging various areas such as the nipples, clitoris, penis or anus, *both before and during intercourse* can bring excellent results. (Have you experimented with this?) Most important ask your lover what turns him or her on.

3. Finding the right rhythm and speed

Due to cultural conditioning, the man still appears to be largely "in charge" of maintaining optimal rhythm and speed during intercourse. However, this is changing. Some couples report excellent result from taking turns. They talk about their needs and offer suggestions. Regardless of who controls the action, moving with the sexual flow and with the partner is of primary importance.

4. Conscious fantasizing and visualizing

Sexual fantasizing is a form of mindplay which involves using mental images having an erotic or sexual content, which are projected on the "screen of the mind." Both genders can use fantasy and visualization to intensify orgasmic release. A considerable number of studies have been published on the use of fantasies during sex.

A hallmark 1986 project involving over 200 married women reached the following conclusion: ". . . sexual fantasies help many married women to achieve sexual arousal and/or orgasm during sexual intercourse, irrespective of their current sex life status." (2) This research, entitled "Sexual Fantasies and Sexual Satisfaction: An Empirical Analysis of Erotic Thought," had participants list their preferred sexual fantasies. The eight most preferred were (not in order of preference):

reliving a sexual experience	extramarital affair
current sex partner	new sex partner

169

more affectionate partner reliving first sexual experience	different coital positions overpowered by acquaintance and forced to sexually surrender

In another study published in 1982, the sexual response of participating women was measured by vaginal photoplethysmography while a) they listened to an erotic tape recording and b) as they were engaged in their individual sexual fantasies. The study concluded: "Those subjects who reported more frequent use of fantasy during masturbation outside the laboratory *showed greater genital responses* during both fantasy and tape elicited arousal than those reporting less use of masturbatory fantasy." (3) Emphasis added.

Some men and women during my interviews volunteered that the deliberate use of fantasies during the sex act intensifies the orgasmic experience. Such fantasies are usually highly private and are rarely communicated to the partner. However, if fantasies can be communicated, they usually serve to deepen the level of intimacy.

Another way to intensify the climax involves visualization, where an individual *consciously* projects a specific image on the mental screen. As one woman put it: "During intercourse I visualize myself having an orgasm. I concentrate on that and presto, I have one! Or I visualize both of us coming together. It works. The orgasm feels stronger."

5. Focusing on feelings

During intercourse, there are a number of primary ways to focus on feelings. Attention can be directed exclusively to the primary site of stimulation or pleasure. "If I concentrate on where the most pleasure is, it builds and builds there. The explosion is incredibly intense."

Another possibility is to focus on the total response. "As we move with each other, my concentration is on what is happening in all parts of my body. I sort of keep what is happening at the genital level like a minor note in a symphony. I listen to it, but mostly I tune in to the whole orchestra. The climax is terrific."

A third possible focus is one's emotions, or the feelings of one's partner. "When we have sex and during the orgasm, I sometimes concentrate completely on my emotions and those of, or about, my partner. Everything else disappears until the unbelievably strong climax." By consciously focusing on the feelings experienced during coitus, an intensification of the climax can be brought about.

6. Vocalizing during the love act

In the U. S. bedroom, vocalizing during the sex act seems to be on the increase. Total silence during intercourse is diminishing; instead, the background noise of television or music from a stereo is preferred by many. Some use these sounds to cover "embarrassing noises." Others eschew background noise in favor of the natural sounds of intercourse, which many find highly erotic.

Most people discover that any type of vocalizing during intercourse intensifies the experience. For example:

"I like to scream and yell when I come like an animal. It makes the orgasm stronger as I do it."

"Messages like 'I love you' make it the best for me."

"I enjoy calling out his name. As I do it, it raises the level of sensations."

"Hearing him turns me on."

"When she starts making those noises I go wild."

7. "Staying at the edge"

The objective is to get close to the point of orgasm as often as four or five times but not to go over the edge and trigger the climax until the tension becomes unbearable. Any of the following interventions can be used to temporarily *postpone* the climax:

171

Stopping and pausing	Pinching or tickling
Slowing stimulation	Stimulating a less sensitive area
Using a lighter touch	Injecting humor

Many lovers have discovered and are continually redis-covering the last of these Fundamental Seven Ways again and again. It may, in fact, be the most effective means of orgasm intensification of them all. (It works best if partners take turns.)

SIXTEEN MORE WAYS OF ORGASM INTENSIFICATION

The means to intensify the orgasm does not stop with the Fundamental Seven listed previously. The following are additional ways to intensify peak ecstasy.

a. Conscious Tension Induction

It has long been known that the orgasm can be intensi-fied by consciously tensing various parts of the body (or the whole body) at the onset of climax. For example, tensing the thighs, legs, or buttocks as the orgasm begins, can have a very marked effect. My experience is that tensing the legs or pushing against the mattress with the buttocks brings excel-lent results. Another way of creating physical tension *is to have intercourse with a very full bladder, thus intensifying the climax.*

b. Influencing the desire pattern

A complexity of physio-psychological factors contribute to build desire to have intercourse. Not surprisingly, these factors vary widely with each person. Young men, for instance, will often describe themselves as "being horny all the time." (Some men appear able to recognize that their seminal pro-duction has reached a state where sexual release is needed.) Women are more likely to find themselves wanting sex just before, during or just after their menstrual periods.

A considerable number of persons view sexual desire as an "animal part' of themselves. They experience difficulty reconciling this animal part with their sexual self-image. As a result, they change sex feelings into those of irritation and discomfort, in a (largely unconscious) attempt to control desire *so* that it is minimal or even absent. The harm done to the psyche by this practice can only be surmised.

In the nineties, people are considerably more free to talk about their feelings of desire. Today, these so-called "animal appetites" are increasingly recognized as normal indicators of sexual health. Members of the younger generations in particular appear to be aware that *the best way to maintain sexual passion is to celebrate its advent.*

Influencing the sexual desire pattern is a very effective way to intensify the orgasmic experience. In this connection, the key question to ask oneself is "What turns me on sexually?" (Long-term couples often fail to address this question periodically, much to the detriment of their sex lives.)

A wide assortment of factors can fuel lust, passion or human sexual desire, including reading erotically arousing literature, viewing porno films, wearing provocative lingerie or nightclothes, or initiating erotic scenarios. (Research suggests that women, like men, are sexually aroused by erotica, but have been socialized to deny or repress it.)

It is well known that when partners have been together for a long time, each tends to know what fuels the sexual passions of the other. Since patterns of sexual arousal can change with the passage of time, long-term couples especially need to periodically ask each other what turns them on.

c. Changing the pattern of arousal or intercourse

All too often, the way long-term couples make love or arouse each other lacks spontaneity and becomes routine. As one wife lamented: "We make love Tuesday, Thursday and Sunday morning. I know every step when he starts out and the two variations in what he is going to do." Because arousal patterns (the sexual routines leading toward the climax) are very pleasantly established, they feel quite comfortable, and the tendency is to maintain them rather than to take the risk of introducing something new.

In January, 1989, the syndicated columnist Ann Landers conducted a survey. She asked her readers the questions: "Has your sex life gone downhill since marriage? If so, why?" She received an unprecedented 141,210 pieces of mail with 52% of the respondents male. (Age range was from 17-93). Eighty-two percent of those replying said that 'Sex after marriage was much less pleasurable. The percentage of unfulfilled females was almost the same as for males." The most frequently recurring adjectives in the replies were "routine," "dull," "monotonous," and "boring."

Any alteration in sexual habits, i.e., changes in arousal techniques, patterns of intercourse, etc. brings best results when preceded by open discussion. A mutual commitment to be open to change is the most important first step. Keeping one's hunger for "something different" in sex a secret, only serves to increase frustration. Instead, a totally objective, no-blame, caring and *honest* discussion can bring forth minor sexual miracles. "We totally changed our usual ways of beginning to make love and have been having honeymoon orgasms."

d. Total sensory immersion

Here, emphasis is on using the maximum of pleasurable inputs to titillate the senses. Some couples insist that this works best if partners take turns. Total sensory immersion can begin with one partner bathing the other, then giving a total body massage, or extended stroking of the body, using a lotion or oil. The use of incense or tantalizing scents, plus romantic music can enhance the sensory experience, as can nibbling on favorite appetizers and tasting preferred beverages early during sex play.

Everything is done unhurriedly, with emphasis on prolonging pleasure. Finally, there is a very slow, loving and extended stimulation of all erogenous zones, with the climax postponed as long as possible. The end result, according to one couple, is a "cosmic orgasm."

e. Timeless and goalessness

To begin the goaless and timeless period, each partner takes however long is needed to create the mental attitude or frame of mind necessary for this type of togetherness. Sometimes this requires private moments or time spent alone at the onset of this experience. A meditative or reflective period can help.

Partners start by creating an atmosphere where they both have no goals other than being together for mutual joy. They flow with events and allow things to happen at their own pace, without pushing or pressure. Sex and orgasm may, or may not, take place. Emphasis here is on the *process,* not the outcomes.

A focus on time and sexual goals has been deeply imbedded in many Western cultures. This is exemplified by the following post-coital observation made by a woman: "I didn't realize until tonight, when he was going down on me, that I had to hurry up with my orgasm or he would get impatient with me. I was programmed, as a woman, to come up with an orgasm and fast. Tonight, for the first time, I realized this and relaxed completely." Men, of course, have the same programming.

Because of this "rush to orgasm" mindset so prevalent in our society, the timeless and goaless way is one of the more difficult means of orgasm intensification to achieve. But for those who seek enhancement of their sexual pleasures, it can result in an extraordinary ecstatic culmination.

f. Innovative abstinence

A period of celibacy-mutually agreed on by a couple-can intensify sexual and orgasmic experiencing. Some couples use an approach called "half-way celibacy," in which they agree on a period of time during which every type of loveplay is indulged in, *except intercourse.* Any type of abstinence fuels sexual desire and passion, while it helps to banish the possibility of either partner being taken (sexually) for granted.

g. Environmental change

A total change in the love-making environment can en-

175

hance the orgasmic experience, especially for long-established couples. Getting away from familiar surroundings and responsibilities is transformative. Going to a motel in another part of the city, or a beautiful spot in the country near mountains, a lake or the ocean, can have a major impact.

The environmental change need not be dramatic. Mini environmental changes, such as transforming the bedroom with branches of trees, bushes and flowers, can also bring excellent results. Couples can avoid the bed and make love on a rug or on the kitchen floor, or backyard lawn. The possibilities for environmental change are endless, and lead to a refreshment of sexual interest.

h. Genital exercises

The genital musculature of the contemporary Western man and woman is, with rare exceptions, an immense land of neglect. The very same people who are walking, jogging, or workout enthusiasts neglect the development of their genital musculature. Both men and women can reap quite extensive sexual benefits by spending a fraction of their time on the development of the muscles that promote the enjoyment of sex.

In the late forties and early fifties, the pioneering physician Arnold Kegel perfected a series of exercises designed to treat women suffering from urinary incontinence, especially after surgery. Kegel found that if women exercised the pubococcygeal (P.C.) muscle which controls the flow of urine, they were able to control their "accidents." Since the P.C. muscle forms the orgasmic platform and contracts during the climax, women also noted an increase in sexual pleasure when they used the Kegel exercises. (Kegel exercises are often recommended after childbirth, both to overcome incontinence and to strengthen the vaginal muscles.)

It took until 1979 for the first empirical research to be published which established a relationship between the P.C. muscle and a woman's orgasmic capacity. Subsequently, sex therapists Georgia Kline-Graber, R.N. and Benjamin Graber, M.D. found that "a major circumvaginal muscle is impaired in women who are unable to achieve orgasm." (4) The findings of the Graber team were consistent with the results of research conducted by sexologists Alice Ladas, Beverly Whipple and John Perry, who concluded that: " . . . the stronger the P. C. muscles, the more likely those women were to experience orgasm as a result of vaginal stimulation." (5)

The best way for women to begin the P.C. exercises is while urinating. Stop the flow for one second and then relax the muscle. Gradually work up to squeezing the muscle for three seconds before allowing it to relax. Then perform a dozen squeezes and releases three times a day. (A variation on this is a quick squeeze and relax, and another quick squeeze and relax, up to ten repetitions, three times a day.) It is also helpful to contract the anal muscles, taking turns with the urinary squeezes.

Another exercise which will strengthen the P.C. muscle is to imagine a tampon in the vagina and then try to push it out. Hold the pushing for three or four seconds. Do this ten times a session, three times a day. Slowly increase the number of "pushes" during each session until you do twenty, three times a day. The pushing exercise can also be done after inserting a finger, dildo or vibrator into the vagina. Using the finger, the muscular contractions of the vagina can be felt. Numerous women reported orgasms solely from P. C. muscle exercises.

Male genitals can also be exercised in a similar manner by stopping urine flow and contracting the anal sphincter muscles. Another variation can be practiced during an erection. Simulate an ejaculation and move the penis back and forth. A small towel, or even a hat, can be suspended from the penis. As the muscles gain in strength, the added weight serves to further exercise the muscles.

The advantages of using genital and anal muscle exercises are two-fold. First, the orgasm is intensified and sexual sensations enhanced. Second, the partner also profits. Since strong vaginal contractions and penile contractions can be felt, this added dimension serves to heighten the other person's erotic pleasure.

i. The use of alcohol and drugs
Studies have shown that alcohol seems to heighten de-

sire or lower some inhibitions when taken in small amounts. Moderate (or greater) amounts of alcohol, however, diminish or take away the ability to perform. This is especially true for men and, to a lesser degree, also true for women. While women can have intercourse regardless of how much they drink, the alcohol in their systems may result in a considerable reduction of their enjoyment level.

The impact on the orgasm of such drugs as amphetamines (speed), LSD (acid) and cocaine appears to vary greatly with the individual. Some people report increased intensification; others a decrease in the ability to perform and to enjoy sex.

Some note a heightening, others a lowering in the intensity of the climax. The effects of marijuana on human sexuality has been more thoroughly researched.

A 1984 hallmark study published in the *Journal of Sex Research,* entitled "Marijuana Use And Sexual Behavior," utilized young, white, middle-class adults. Over 80% worked full time in a variety of occupations. The subjects (average age 27.5 years) averaged over two years of marijuana use. As a part of the study, ten research projects conducted in the seventies were summarized. Consistent findings were that the use of marijuana was associated with increased sexual desire and sexual enjoyment. The 1984 study's findings are summarized as follows: "Over two thirds (of 97 subjects) reported increased sexual pleasure and satisfaction with marijuana. Increased desire for a familiar sexual partner was reported by about one half." (6)

j. The Water Jet experience
The hand-held shower head and particularly the hot tub spa with its pulsating water jets are two of California's greatest contributions to the female orgasm. (See also the section on *orgasm tone,* Chapter 7, pp. 141-142). Female aficionados of the Jacuzzi often make this discovery by accident. Then, elated by their discovery, they can repeat the experience at their leisure.

One lady of my acquaintance would emerge from the spa with a special rosy glow on her face. When questioned, she revealed that she used a certain strategically placed jet to induce orgasm. "It's a different feeling, very intense. And I can have it any time." One morning we awakened to the loud cries and moans of someone in the throes of sexual ecstasy. We rushed to the balcony overlooking the yard to discover her daughter, who was in her late teens, in the spa. She was in orgasmic communion with the spa jet and appeared oblivious to all else. "As the mother, so the daughter," was my not so bright comment. Whether or not the girl had learned this from her mother, or on her own, was never disclosed.

k. Focusing on love and caring

When especially affectionate and loving feelings are dominant in a relationship, an increase in orgasm intensity is often noted. One couple reported that on those occasions when they were especially pleased with, or feeling good about each other, they invariably talked about their love before having intercourse. They focused on the good moments they had mutually experienced, such as unexpected windfalls, minor successes, achievements of their children, etc. The man reported that "The climax is always the best ever." This is not altogether surprising, since, in most instances, *the intensity of the orgasm is directly related to the extent of the individuals' emotional involvement.*

l. Orgasm extension

For a man, an orgasm can be intensified (and extended) if his partner alternately stimulated his penis manually (before) and the prostate digitally before and during intercourse. A woman may achieve the same results if her G-Spot and clitoris are both alternately stimulated manually before intercourse.

m. Relaxation before sex

The climax can sometimes be intensified if one or both partners can achieve total relaxation before making love. Techniques which give good results are massage, meditation and any type of muscle relaxation which involves the entire body.

Contrary to popular opinion, soaking in a hot tub or Jacuzzi, while fostering relaxation, may have a negative effect on sexual energy. A man may become too relaxed to perform. (For those who insist on a quick dip in hot waters, a cold shower afterward can enhance the erotic drive and stimulate the libido.)

n. Breathing right

The tendency, during intercourse, is to breathe shallowly or even to periodically hold the breath. Deep breathing during love-making, on the other hand, can sometimes intensify the orgasm. This takes some practice until such deep breathing comes naturally. Another alternative is "pelvic breathing." When one partner thrusts toward the other, the thrusting partner exhales (breathes out).

o. Exploring Asian Thrust Formulas

Asian formulas for male thrusting often intensify the orgasm. The man mentally divides the vagina into three levels: shallow, middle and deep. In the first Asian formula, he does nine shallow thrusts followed by a deep one. In the second formula, he does seven shallow thrusts followed by one deep one. Whichever formula he selects should be repeated throughout the coital act as opposed to using it just once. The Asian formulas vary widely in bringing desired results. They work with some, but not with others.

p. The Pushout Technique

There is another simple way for women to intensify their orgasms. It is by using the Pushout Technique ("pushing out" as in childbirth.) This consists of pushing out with both the vaginal and anal sphincters as the orgasm commences. For many women who have experimented with this technique, pushing out the vaginal sphincter brings excellent results.

Other women report their most intensive climax is achieved from pushing out with both anal and vaginal sphincters at the same time. (Several sexologists have mentioned this method for orgasm intensification.) This raises an interesting question: do some men experience an intensification of their orgasms when contracting or pushing out with their anal sphincters?

q. The Use of Sex Toys

According to the latest survey, one out of ten Americans are now using sex toys. There have been consistent reports by men and women that the use of such toys has resulted in orgasm intensification. A number have also reported that having new experiences with sex toys has resulted in changes from mono- or polyorgasmic experiencing to becoming hetero-orgasmic.

Orgasm intensification has remained a neglected art precisely because it requires a certain amount of sexual self-exploration as well as sexual self-understanding and discipline. Some people intensify their orgasms "by accident," but do not make any effort to understand, remember and repeat it. The development of the potential to intensify an orgasm may be opposed by an individual's social anti-pleasure conditioning or belief system. Such a person may believe that orgasms which "just happen" are okay (i.e., natural and thus normal), while orgasms which are deliberately intensified are *not* okay, but deemed to be unnatural (i.e., perverse or sinful in some way). Regardless of such limiting perspectives, the area of orgasm intensification presents an interesting challenge for sexual self-development and orgasm shaping, with a very rewarding foreseeable outcome: the heightening of sexual ecstasy.

Notes

1. Mary Jo Sholty, Paul H. Ephros, Michael Plant, Susan M. Fischman, Jane F. Charnas, Carol A Cody, "Female Orgasmic Experience: A Subjective Study," *Archives of Sexual behavior,* 2 (1984): 159.

2. J. Kenneth Davidson, Sr. and Linda E. Hoffman, "Sexual Fantasies and Sexual Satisfaction: An Empirical Analysis of Erotic Thought, *Journal of Sex Research, 2* (1986):184,197.

3. Wendy E. Stock and James H. Geer, "A Study of Fantasy-Based Sexual Arousal in Women," *Archives of Sexual Behavior, 1,* (1982): 33.

4. Georgia Kline-Graber and Benjamin Graber, *Women's Orgasm,* (Warner Books, 1983): 349.

5. Alice K. Ladas, Beverly Whipple and John D. Perry, *The G Spot,* (Holt, Rhinehart, Winston, 1982): 122.

6. Ronald A. Weller and James A. Halikas, "Marijuana Use and Sexual Behavior," *The Journal of Sex Research,* 2 (1984): 186.

CHAPTER 10

METHODS FOR EXTENDING THE LIBERATED ORGASM SPECTRUM
Part I

This chapter contains notes on the developmental nature of the climax, as well as guidelines for extending the liberated orgasm spectrum. Two highly effective methods the Orgasm Articulation Method and Fusion Orgasm Training are then discussed.

Using methods for extending the orgasm spectrum is an easy and pleasurable way to become involved in sexual self-development. Throughout your adventure with sexual self-development, use your intuition while selecting the areas and specific ways you will use to extend the horizon of your sexual experiencing. Let intuition be your guide. Open yourself and keep this in mind as you read this and the next chapter. Finally, be sure to communicate all your intuitive perceptions to your partner.

Sexual pleasure and the orgasm are rooted both in the sexual nervous system and the psyche. They are a creation which draws on components of the sexual belief system, past sexual (and related) experiences, as well as the imagination and fantasy. In short, during sex, psychological factors play a primary role. Everyone has the potential to develop new climactic options, liberate the orgasm and join the orgasmic revolution.

Since orgasms comprise some of the most, if not *the* most ecstatic sensual moments human beings are able to experience, they deserve our devotion and development. This is especially appropriate since the human climax has finally begun to come out of the closet. This and the following chapter offer eight new methods to develop, shape and enjoy more of the full spectrum of the orgasmic rainbow.

183

The first step is to be aware of the developmental nature of the climax and to believe that the human orgasm can be liberated and its spectrum extended. It is strongly suggested that anyone interested in exploring and extending the orgasmic rainbow re-read the section on "Resistance to the Liberated Orgasm," (Chapter 2, pp. 26-28) and "The Discovery of the Orgasmic States of Being and the Shaping of the Orgasm: A Learning Process," (Chapter 7, pp.132-138).

Before proceeding with methods for extending the liberated orgasm spectrum, a word of caution is necessary. In today's society, it is easy to succumb to the temptation to develop one's sexual potential *in a competitive way,* by, for example, subscribing to the belief that people who experience a larger spectrum of orgasms are sensually superior. This belief fosters a type of competition which injects pressure and tension into the process of developing one's sexual capacities. It is indisputable that people's orgasm patterns vary tremendously. Someone with a capacity to experience many types of orgasms *is not necessarily a better lover, nor is he or she sexually superior.*

THE DEVELOPMENTAL NATURE OF THE CLIMAX—"THE ORGASM CAN BE SHAPED"

Although our ostensible focus is pleasure, people often find that exploration of sexual potential requires courage and integrity.
                    -Sexologist David Schnarch

As has been repeatedly mentioned, *the many-dimensional qualities of the human orgasm can, to a considerable extent, be shaped, formed and created by the individual.* The nature of the climax is influenced, among others things, by a person's moods, emotional state and physical condition (especially fatigue). It is also clear that the nature of the orgasm *changes.* A sensitive awareness to this process can be deliberately cultivated. This can be done while bringing conscious change to various components of the orgasm, both to extend and enrich this event.

Developing Orgasm Awareness

Developing the orgasm first requires developing *orgasm awareness, or the ability to become keenly aware of what transpires during the climax.* This includes the ability to describe what has happened during the climax, after it has taken place. For some, this is difficult since they experience peak pleasure only as a quickly passing state of chaotic ecstasy. Paying close attention and directing conscious attention into this process will lead to the realization that the seeming chaos of ecstasy has numerous complexities.

Concentrating on what goes on during the orgasmic event, followed by verbally sharing with a partner what transpired, and/or writing down what has happened, are major steps in building orgasm awareness and the development, or shaping, of the climax. Such action demands courage plus discipline and will take time to open these new doors of sensory perception. However, acquiring a sharpened awareness of the intricacies and splendors of the climax is well worth the investment of energy and effort.

Four Important Elements

The developmental nature of the human orgasm is illuminated by five major signposts, as follows.

1. The Orgasmic States of Being

Large numbers of individuals have characteristic or habitual ways of experiencing the climax and have described them. Seven major orgasmic states of being have been identified to date (see Chapter 7, pp. 127-129). Others will undoubtedly be discovered. Be aware that the orgasmic states of being are subject to change due to the life experiences of the individual they are thus also developmental in nature.

2. The Intensity or Strength of the Climax

Orgasm intensification is a neglected art of pleasure enhancement. It is also a highly individualistic matter. Twenty-three ways of heightening the climactic experience are described in Chapter 9, pp. 167-181. Orgasms routinely vary in intensity, but the degree of intensity can be shaped.

185

3. Trigger Component Attributes and Orgasm Discrimination

The human sexual nervous system is highly complex. It incorporates various components, including the mouth, the breasts, the clitoris, the vagina, the G-Spot, the penis, the anus and the psyche (which can create a mental orgasm). Any of these can, through training, be utilized to trigger an orgasm.

Orgasm discrimination is the ability to distinguish between different types of orgasms—those triggered by different sexual nervous system components. There is evidence that this ability can be learned. Those who have this ability are said to be *hetero-orgasmic*. In other words, they can have a climax from stimulation of more than one component of the sexual nervous system, with each orgasm having distinctive, unique characteristics linked to the source of stimulation.

In contrast, those individuals who are *mono-orgasmic* climax from stimulation of only one of the components of the sexual nervous system. In the third group are *poly-orgasmic* individuals who, while capable of having a climax from stimulation of more than one source, report *that all climaxes feel the same.*

4. Peak Pleasure Time Flow

Some individuals have an awareness of the flow of time as they experience an orgasm. For some, the climax is experienced as lasting for a brief period, while for others it seems to last a long time. Still others describe a state of *orgasmic infinity*-there seems to be no beginning or end to the climax and it appears to "last forever." There are indications that the individual has the option to determine the subjective nature of the orgasmic time flow.

The tremendous energies of the climax can also be channeled in certain directions, and the individual's creative capacities appear to play the role in this process. The mental set, the intent and purposes by which this energy is channeled can shape the type of climactic experience which results. In China and India, for example, practitioners of Taoist rites and Tantric Yoga, have, for centuries, used sacred rituals to shape the orgiastic experience. Most people in Western as well as Eastern cultures, however, use only a small portion of their sexual belief and energy system for sexual gratification and to add richness and variety to the climax.

Not everyone is amenable to the improvement of their sexual capacity. This is not surprising, in view of the social taboos and proscriptions about sex which are so widespread. It takes courage to overcome these, plus discipline, and persistence to develop sexual potential.

It must be remembered that the exquisite sensation of "being out of control" which accompanies the climax is NOT lost by acquiring the capacity for conscious orgasm shaping or development. It has been firmly established that returning to the usual experiencing of orgasmic states of being such as "Chaotic Ecstasy" (Chapter 7, p. 127) is always readily available. It must be clear that one aspect of conscious orgasm development involves *acquiring the option to select a specific type of orgasmic state of being and to a considerable extent shaping the content or flow of the selected climactic experience.*

Another aspect of orgasmic development consists of choosing a component of the sexual nervous system (not previously used to achieve climax.) Then *using various means so that stimulation can trigger the particular type of peak ecstasy which is characteristic of the component.* The fact that the climax is developmental opens a number of doors to the creative practitioner who is interested in exploring the infinite hidden universe of the human peak ecstasy.

The question, 'Since the orgasm is such a peak pleasure moment, why develop it at all?" is a recurrent one. This notion that climactic pleasure is so great that it cannot or need not be developed further is called the *camouflage effect of the climax.* (See Chapter 2, p. 28). Part of the answer to this question is that, despite all safeguards, there is a tendency, sooner or later, for boredom to creep into the precincts of sexual experiencing. Making love to the same partner in the same way in the same bed night after night eventually becomes more of a habit than a special occasion.

The libido, like the palate, finds variety and new erotic experiences the spice of life. As a result, many if not most people will welcome an enhancement of their sexual pleasure *especially if this is an enhancement they can enjoy for- the rest of their sex life.* Exploring the universe of the orgasm, plus using orgasm shaping, can be an exciting adventure for the rest of one's life.

GUIDELINES FOR EXTENDING THE LIBERATED ORGASM SPECTRUM

It will be recalled that the hetero-orgasmic individual is able to have orgasms from the stimulation of a variety of components of the sexual nervous system, and each climax feels different than the other. Who will become hetero-orgasmic? Women are in a better position than men to make the transition from mono-orgasmic, to poly or hetero-orgasmic functioning. They have more socially sanctioned orgasm possibilities than do men. If, for example, a woman is only able to have an orgasm as the result of clitoral stimulation, she has any number of options to expand her orgasmic experiencing: a breast orgasm, a G-Spot orgasm, an anal orgasm, etc.

The man is not so fortunate. It has been his life-long social conditioning to believe that he is capable only of a penile orgasm. Many men react to the idea that they are capable of other types of orgasms by feeling threatened or anxious. Macho males appear to be especially threatened. For numerous, if not most men, the *only* socially-sanctioned male orgasm, for the foreseeable future, will remain the penile climax. They will have little interest in other options.

There is no guaranteed prescription for the transition from mono-orgasmic or poly-orgasmic functioning to hetero-orgasmic functioning. The task of the individual is to learn *orgasm discrimination.* To repeat, many variables play a role in making such a transition, including one's upbringing and sex history, as well as the intercourse belief system and other components. For this reason, the so-called "shot gun approach" is likely to yield the best results. *The shotgun approach consists of trying out a variety of means and methods to extend the orgasm spectrum until one of them 'hits the target."* For example, use of the various orgasm intensification exercises covered in Chapter

9, pp.172-181, have resulted in mono- or poly-orgasmic people becoming hetero-orgasmic.

Extending the capacity for orgasmic experiencing works best if it is done in a playful, spirit one of fun and adventure. The guidelines presented in this section will prevent difficulties while enhancing sexual enjoyment.

Expanding or extending one's orgasm range or learning orgasm discrimination may best be done by oneself rather than in the presence of a partner. Many couples who have spent numerous years together may discover areas of sexual anxiety and shame which can present problems when they are engaged in an adventure of sexual self-development, while acting as a team.

For example, study after study has shown that masturbation is a very common practice of one or both partners in most unions. Sexologists have long recommended that couples masturbate to orgasm in front of each other as a means of breaking down barriers and facilitating the fulfillment of sexual needs. Yet comparatively few heterosexual couples appear to have done this, or do this.

Unless both Partners feel sufficiently comfortable to stimulate themselves to orgasm in front of each other, it is strongly suggested that the adventure of extending their orgasm range be pursued independently by each partner. Here are two additional guidelines:
1. Go to and develop the erotic spot where there has been a history of high sexual excitement.

"I chose the breast orgasm for development because I almost came that way in my teens and before we got married."

"When I first read the book about the G-Spot, I started experimenting and found the spot. I got excited, but didn't get around to an orgasm. It's a good place to start."

"I enjoy anal stimulation during sex and I'll work on this one."

189

2. Make this exploration an enjoyable occasion and be patient with yourself, it takes time to change.

"We like our sex life but there's always room for improvement, so we decided to try something new we could both enjoy. One exercise didn't work for him. The other got results."

"We kept playing around with the exercises in the spirit of fun and it worked."

As mentioned earlier, the use of self-stimulation may be necessary to extend the orgasm spectrum and to develop *orgasm discrimination, the capacity to distinguish between different types of orgasms.* According to many men and women, the climax achieved through self-stimulation feels different compared to other climaxes. This has also been observed by a small minority of mono- and polyorgasmic individuals. Although many describe the experience of self-pleasuring as "more intense," the majority appear to place the masturbatory orgasm on a hierarchic scale while labeling this difference as "inferior."

A number of participants in the orgasm spectrum research noted that using new variations in techniques, or ways of self-stimulation, helped them develop orgasm discrimination. Ways of stimulation not previously used appear to be especially effective. While doing this, it is helpful to focus total concentration on the sexual sensations and feelings as they run their course (Communicate what happened during this process).

One man reported that he had never used a vibrator on his penis. He believed that "this strange new feeling" which he experienced for the first time, subsequently helped him to move from mono-orgasmic to hetero-orgasmic functioning. Numerous women had similar experiences. Many reported achieving an orgasm from directing a water jet toward the clitoris for the first time.

Several of the women used a Waterpik, a teeth-cleaning apparatus which has adjustable water jet pressure. It is possible that the "newness" of such experiences breaks old patterns of perception and changes the belief system. In other words, the individual has *experienced* that an orgasm can feel different from previous orgasms.

It is not unusual for a lifetime to be spent without ever attempting to describe the climactic event. Some people also believe that an orgasm is very private and for various reasons should not be described, or is too hard to describe. There may consequently be strong resistance to putting this experience into words.

"I didn't want to do it and had to use will-power to get it into words."

"Why talk when you can just lie there and enjoy the afterglow? But then I went ahead anyway. There was a lot of stammering and pauses. After the third time trying to describe the orgasm, some amazing things began to happen."

It is important to remember that, for most of us, it is not easy to articulate about these very intimate and special moments. Patience and repeated practice are needed. The building of a conceptual/verbal or descriptive vocabulary about what happens during the climax takes time and practice.

The sequence of becoming aware of what takes place during the orgasm and then describing this, appears to *open or develop new neurological connections.* At the same time, it is a way of extending and developing the discriminatory system, or capacity for distinguishing differences which take place during the sequence of events which constitute the orgasmic process. Briefly put, it fosters the evolution of the orgasm to consciously focus directive awareness into the experience and to verbally describe its form after it has happened. You may wish to explore the following:

How did you feel during the orgasm?

What went on in your body?

191

Were there stages or phases in your orgasm?

Did you have fantasies or mental images during the climax?

THE ORGASM ARTICULATION METHOD

Articulation of what takes place during the orgasmic process, repeated over seven to nine post-orgasmic sessions, can begin to bring subtle positive change to the climax itself. (For many it may take more sessions until change is noticed, while others become aware of immediate, subtle changes.) Finally, use of the three basic principles can help in achieving voluntary control of the orgasmic states of being. (See Chapter 7, p. 127).

This is a highly effective method which needs repeated and routine use for maximum results. Use of the method, over a period of time, deepens sexual sensitivity, self-awareness and understanding. Talking about the orgasm and describing the experience is a way of learning *orgasm awareness,* which, in turn, deepens intimacy while strengthening couple closeness.

There have been numerous reports of another effect linked to the use of this method. A type of <u>associated recall</u> is fostered. Talking about the peak pleasure of the climax seems to make accessible other peak moments in life. Many couples enjoy sharing them.

Each partner needs to clearly understand that the use of this method is for purposes of sexual self-development, and that the responsibility for what happens during orgasm is essentially that of the person describing the experience. (Care needs to be taken to protect each other from the notion that the partner is responsible for the quality or content of the climax.)

It is again strongly recommended that those who wish to pursue the adventure of extending and enriching their orgasmic experiencing review the section entitled "The Orgasmic States of Being," Chapter 7, pp.127-129, plus the section entitled "The Discovery of the Orgasmic States of Being—A Learning process" (Chapter 7, pp. 132-136). The Orgasm Articulation Method has two parts:

1) First, it is necessary to direct conscious attention into the processes or event we call the climax. This means becoming aware of the different sensations, feelings, images etc. which take place. To a certain extent, this also involves becoming an observer of this flow of happening.

2) The next step is to describe how the orgasm felt and what took place during the climax after it is over. This means talking about and describing the experience to the partner (or writing it out in detail.)

Some couples who have not previously done so, may have some difficulty sharing the sensations, images and fantasies they have during the climax. Most people find it hard, initially, to describe the climax. This is not surprising because the chaos of ecstasy, at first, seems to defy description. The capacity of becoming acutely aware of what transpires during the climactic experience imparts a new splendor and brilliance to the happening. Use of the Orgasm Articulation Method is one of the most rewarding ways of shaping, enriching and eventually extending the peak moments of sexual ecstasy.

"The fantasies changed and seemed to last longer."

"I became aware of ebbs and flows and rhythms when it was happening, like never before."

"After the seventh time I talked about it, there was a new crispness and strength in the sensations. Something new had been added."

FUSION ORGASM TRAINING

The blended, or *fusion* orgasm occurs when two (or more) sexual nervous system components are *simultaneously* stimulated toward peaking, resulting in a climax which encompasses both of them. The fusion orgasm has unique and distinct characteristics, differing from those of an orgasm produced from stimulating one of these sources alone.

Fusion orgasm training works extremely well for those who are capable of a climax from two or more different sources, although others can also use this method to obtain excellent results. The goal here is to try to coordinate the two (potential) orgasms as much as possible, with a focus, or intent, to blend them into one. A complete blending of the two erotic feeling components is rarely achieved nor is it necessary. However, the intent to do this can result in a climax that is often twice as intense as an orgasm resulting from one source alone. As in other exercises, a combination of patience and repeated practice will bring the desired outcome.

Quite often, during simultaneous stimulation of two erotically sensitive components, one of them is "faster." That is, stimulation of both components reveals that a climax *will more speedily result* from stimulation of just one of these sources. In such instances, it is best to stop, or slow down, stimulation of the "fast source" and concentrate on the other. As previously noted, the intent is the important element.

For most women, using the clitoral and vaginal/cervical orgasms for the fusing is easiest. During a preliminary "warm-up" period, the clitoris can be manipulated with one hand while, at the same time pumping fingers or a phallic shaped object in and out of the vagina. Another possibility for women is the breast/clitoral fusion orgasm. (Other combinations of the Basic Seven are also an option.)

It is a bonus of the fusion orgasm that those who once experience it often prefer it to other climaxes they are capable of having. *Many women will be able to considerably improve their climactic repertoire* by as much as 200 to 300 percent, through using methods contained in this and the following chapter.

The man's choice for a fusion orgasm is more severely limited. As mentioned earlier, *due to social conditioning and indoctrination,* men are largely restricted to believe they can have only the penile orgasm. Sex education courses largely continue to teach the traditional, now totally outdated, historical orgasm framework. For men especially, the following applies: *in order to experience the liberated orgasm, you must both know about it and believe that it is possible.*

The prostate or anal/penile, the mouth/penile or breast/penile orgasms are the man's obvious choices for fusion orgasm training. For most men, using the prostate or anal orgasm along with penile stimulation appears to bring results most quickly. Reports indicate that men also experience the fusion orgasm as more intense.

This chapter has discussed two of the most effective initial ways by which the orgasmic rainbow can be extended. The next chapter will focus on additional exercises designed to further facilitate the potential for expanding orgasmic pleasure.

CHAPTER 11

METHODS FOR EXTENDING THE LIBERATED ORGASM SPECTRUM
Part II

Liberating the orgasm from the shackles of wrong information plus dysfunctional attitudes, deeply established habits and erroneous beliefs, does not happen overnight. Some effort is required, but the rewards are well worth it. This chapter contains additional exercises which lead to the actualizing of orgasmic potential for both men and women. They are The New Pathway Procedure, The Man's Climax Postponement Exercise, the Woman's Climax Postponement Exercise, the Orgasm Tone Experience, the Contraction Prolongation Exercise, Pre-Orgasmic Pleasure Balloon Extension, and the Orgasm Diary. Finally there is the G-Spot Orgasm Development exercise. It has been added because many, if not most women, have not as yet developed their G-Spot climax.

THE NEW PATHWAY PROCEDURE

This exercise is designed for those who wish to develop new neural pathways which have not as yet (or rarely) been utilized to achieve a climax. The goal here is to investigate and develop previously relatively unexplored components of the sexual nervous system, thereby extending the orgasm spectrum. This procedure is especially recommended for mono-orgasmic men and women who wish to become poly- or hetero-orgasmic, and poly-orgasmic individuals interested in becoming hetero-orgasmic. Again, as with the other exercises in this volume, patience and repeated practice is recommended. Extending the orgasm spectrum, like the building of

Rome-will not be accomplished in one day. (Note: use of the climax postponement exercises described in the next section will help facilitate success with the new pathway procedure.)

The first step is to *select the sexual nervous system component you wish to develop as a source of orgasm.* Start with the area which, in the past, has yielded the most sexual pleasure without orgasm. If a woman, for example, usually climaxes only from clitoral stimulation, but has also experienced much pleasure from breast or nipple play in the past, a good choice for her would be to develop the breast as a new neural pathway to orgasm. She would begin by spending at least two (private) sessions self-pleasuring her breasts and nipples *to discover which type of stimulation is particularly arousing.* Emphasis would be on exploration and development, not on attempting to reach a breast orgasm.

The next step would be to stimulate the breast, nipples *and* clitoris *simultaneously.* Two to five sessions would be devoted to the interplay of these two areas. Again, there would be no focus on achieving a breast orgasm. A clitoral orgasm, while fully stimulating the breasts, would conclude each session.

The third step involves getting as close to a clitoral orgasm as possible while maintaining a very high nipple/breast stimulation. At the last possible moment before the clitoral climax, stop or diminish clitoral stimulation, and continue to vigorously stimulate the breast and nipples. While using this procedure, four or more sessions may be needed before the breast orgasm is triggered, thus taking precedence over the clitoral. Others succeed in less time.

The procedure for the man is similar. His choice is usually between developing a prostate, anal, mouth, or breast orgasm. The following is my detailed written account about what happened when I became interested in developing a prostate orgasm.

"While a graduate student, I sought treatment for a prostate infection. A proctologist massaged the gland repeatedly for some weeks. The treatment was painful. After graduating, I became professionally active. I am an avid reader and several years later I came across some interesting references in my reading. Several authors mentioned that anal and prostate stimulation was experienced as pleasurable by many heterosexual as well as homosexual men. I then remembered the enemas administered by my mother during early childhood. They always caused an erection. The sensual affect surrounding the administration of enemas during my childhood appears to have had the effect of heightening my anal sensitivity.

I also recalled that on several occasions, women had played with my anus prior to and during intercourse and that I had enjoyed this. I decided to explore my anal and prostate sensitivity as fully as possible. Using the lubricated index finger, it took several tries to locate the prostate gland. When touched or gently massaged, initially there was a strange, not very pleasing and unfamiliar sensation. I persisted in gentle stimulation for several occasions and slowly, pleasurable feelings began to emerge. This took about four to six sessions.

In subsequent sessions of self-stimulation, I began to notice a sort of "full," slightly pleasurable feeling, which was beginning to develop in the head of my penis as I stroked my prostate. This was encouraging, *as obviously a connection was being established in the sexual nervous system between the prostate and the penis.* After another four to six sessions of prostate stroking, it was clear that a relatively low level of pleasurable feelings had been established between the prostate and the head of the penis. These sensations, however, had reached a plateau.

The low level of pleasure I felt did not seem to increase and I decided to try another route to further establish and extend the conditioning between penis and prostate. Stimulating the penis and prostate in turn, or *alternately, as well as simultaneously* greatly increased the pleasure. Persistence in this procedure slowly began to yield more intense pleasure both in the prostate and the head of the penis.

199

I now experimented with the simultaneous stimulation of the penis and prostate (using fingers and later a dildo) while masturbating to orgasm. This caused an increase in the pleasure of the climax. I had noticed that, up to a point, the pleasure feelings were different but then 'the penis took over.' The penile orgasm felt as usual, although sometimes stronger.

It then occurred to me to try another approach to forging a stronger link between the two pleasure centers. I decided to masturbate almost to orgasm by stimulating the penis, then stroke the prostate to trigger the climax. The first time I tried this, I did not insert my finger in the anus until I was close to orgasm from manual penile stimulation. This procedure did not seem to work very well as it yielded the usual penile climax.

Then I realized that excitement of the prostate had to be maintained (by continuous stimulation) at the same time penile stimulation took place. On the next try, after almost reaching a penile climax manually, I was able to trigger the orgasm through further vigorous prostate stroking. The prostate orgasm was entirely different from the usual penile climax. It was much "duller," and not as intense.

Also, when the orgasm was triggered by the prostate, the ejaculate dribbled out, without the usual strong penile contractions. which had propelled the ejaculate some distance. Nevertheless, I experienced this climax as something new and different from my usual penile orgasms. At this point I had acquired *orgasm discrimination* and had become *hetero-orgasmic..*

I persisted in trying to develop the prostate orgasm further. Refraining from all sexual activity for a week, I then attempted to stimulate a prostate orgasm using only the finger I had inserted. This took a long time and was fatiguing, but finally the orgasm occurred. It was the same "dull" prostate climax previously experienced. Next, I used a vibrator with the same results.

It became clear that this type of orgasm was, for me, an interesting variation from the usual penile one, and was to be experienced every once in a while. With the passage of years, I gradually had less desire to experience this orgasm since it lacked intensity. The enjoyment of anal play, however, continued undiminished and increased. On reflection, it seems that *the painful prostate massage by a proctologist when I was a graduate student was responsible for the low level of orgasmic intensity and pleasure from the prostate.*

To briefly summarize the three steps of the New Pathway procedure:

Step 1. Explore the full erotic potential of the sexual nervous system component selected for development to discover what type of stimulation is most pleasurable (2-4 or more sessions.)

Step 2: Stimulate the selected component simultaneously with a component which usually triggers orgasm, with emphasis on learning their interplay. Make no attempt to attain orgasm from the selected component (for 2-5 more sessions) and conclude the sessions with a climax from the component which usually triggers orgasm.

Step 3: Simultaneously stimulate the usual source of orgasm and the selected component, maintaining a high level of excitation in both. Then focus on the build-up of the climax (while continuing to stimulate the selected component), stopping just short of orgasm. At this point, stimulate the selected component more vigorously to trigger a climax. (Four or more sessions may be needed.)

PEAK ECSTASY POSTPONEMENT

Exercises which serve to postpone the climax not only heighten and intensify the peak moment, they also establish an additional measure of control. For men, this latter element is of special importance. Many if not most men appear to have little control over the length of time from intromission of the penis into the vagina to the "point of no return" when orgasm is inevitable. The climax postponement exercise for men, after repeated practice, will prolong the erection and provide more control about when the orgasm will take place.

Climax postponement exercises are of equal value to help women gain a greater sense of control over their climax. In fact, some women reported a lessening of "orgasm anxiety" as a result of using this exercise. Climax postponement exercises can, of course, also be done as a couple. However, when a couple does not feel totally comfortable about masturbating in each other's presence, it is best to do these exercises alone.

The Man's Climax Postponement Exercise

This particular exercise both lengthens erotic pleasure and intensifies the orgasm. Another outcome has consistently been reported. With repeated use of this method, some men who had complained of premature ejaculations, found they no longer had the problem.

Fear of being discovered while masturbating during adolescence has conditioned men (and women) to hasten the self-pleasuring process. Very often, when the man becomes an adult, the sense of urgency which has been established in youth is carried over and pervades intercourse, largely on an unconscious basis. The good news is that this pattern of haste is reversible. Simply set aside a block of time and approach self-pleasuring in a leisurely, relaxed manner and prolong what feels good as long as possible. Do it several times to establish this on an attitudinal level.

Another common error made by many men is that they

grasp the penis too tightly while masturbating. To approximate the vaginal environment, it is best for the pressure on the penis not to exceed that of a firm handshake. It is also helpful to use a lotion to approximate vaginal moisture.

Begin by pleasuring yourself as if you had "all the time in the world." The intent of this exercise is to *prolong penile pleasure,* not to ejaculate. Focus your awareness on the pleasure. Stop when you sense you are close to the point of no return (ejaculatory inevitability). Now use the *squeeze technique.* Grasp the head of the penis with the first two fingers on the underside and the thumb at the top of the penis. Now squeeze tightly and hold the pressure for about twenty seconds. In response to this treatment, the penis may either grow in size, become limp, or change to an intermediate state of firmness. (The pleasure level of the penis is diminished by this procedure.)

Following the squeeze, resume the motion of your hand as you continue masturbating. (Do this even if you do not have an erection.) The intent of the exercise is to prolong the pleasure of penile stimulation as long as possible. At first, try to maintain an erection, using the squeeze technique when indicated, to prolong self-pleasuring for at least 5-10 minutes, or more. In subsequent sessions, aim for longer time periods of experiencing penile pleasure.

As you make noticeable gains (usually about the third or fourth session), use the squeeze technique even closer to the point of ejaculatory inevitability. Make it a challenge to get as close to this point as you can, without triggering the orgasm. On resuming stroking the penis, push a bit closer to the point of no return (ejaculatory inevitability). Be sure to have a lengthy pause before resuming.

Many men also find they have to wait until the next time they use this exercise to resume penile stimulation. (The stimulation of the penis while beginning this exercise results in a high level of excitation which may persist and may not be diminished by a lengthy pause.)

Another very effective means, which can be used in conjunction with the preceding, involves using certain *physical and mental interventions.* You can, for example, pinch yourself when you are approaching the climax to interrupt the pleasure flow. Tickling yourself or asking your partner to do so, is another possibility. Or you could tickle your partner, etc.

Steven Change, author of *The Tao Of Sexology,* found that some men successfully use the (physical intervention) of pressure on the perineum. This is the area in front of the anus extending to the genitals.

Any form of distraction which interrupts the build-up of the flow of sexual pleasure can be used. Some men do mathematical problems or they may count sheep (or clitorises), jumping over a fence, etc. Others try joking or even singing (see also Chapter 9, pp. 171-172). Continue these practices until you reach ejaculatory control i.e. you know when the climax will take place and you can postpone it.

The Woman's Climax Postponement Exercise

The vast majority of women do not need to use this exercise. This especially in view of the fact that so many cannot have an orgasm from intercourse alone. However, a small minority of women know that *learning to postpone their climax, can vastly increase the intensity of their orgasms* (see also Chapter 9, pp. 171-172). This section is dedicated to this minority.

Begin by setting a block of time aside for leisurely and relaxed pleasuring of yourself. Use self-stimulation to get as close to having a climax as you can, but stop yourself before the orgasm begins.

The focus is on increasing control over your climax without reaching the point of culmination. As you do this, *you will become more sensitive to what is happening in your body* as you approach the climax. A variation on this exercise is to postpone the climax as long as possible and at that point use the P.C. muscle exercise (see Chapter 9, pp. 176-177). This provides the additional benefit of strengthening the muscles.

THE ORGASM TONE EXPERIENCE

Orgasm tone involves the utilization of a special element (such as a vibrator or dildo), to induce the climax, adding a particular feeling tone which distinguishes such a climax from all other orgasms. Reports and interviews indicated that many people experienced a type of orgasm *which differed fundamentally* from other climaxes when using a vibrator, certain implements, or sex toys. This was also reported by a number of mono-orgasmic and poly-orgasmic individuals. Many of the latter, as a consequence of using various implements, sex toys and other means, discovered they had become hetero-orgasmic as the result of such sexperimentation.

It will be recalled that orgasm tone was briefly discussed in Chapter Seven, pp.141-142. The orgasm tone experience involves experimenting with a range of special means in order to trigger a climax which, as a result, distinguishes it from all other orgasms. Use of the following may induce such a climax:

Water jets

Textured condoms

Anal beads

Cock rings

Vibrators

Ben Wa balls

Textured dildos (etc.)

Becoming involved with this experience provides an enjoyable and adventurous form of sexual self-development. It will also extend the capacity for experiencing new aspects of the liberated orgasm spectrum.

THE CONTRACTION PROLONGATION EXERCISE

This exercise is very effective for both men and women. Its use can result in both the prolongation of climactic pleasure as well as increasing control over the nature of the orgasm. A final benefit is that, for some, it results in intensification of the climax.

Instructions for use of this exercise are quite simple.

When the orgasmic contractions begin, flow with them, then continue the muscular genital contractions on a voluntary basis as long as possible. Women should use will power and muscular control by consciously squeezing the vagina.

Similarly, when orgasm begins, men can "pump" the penis, using penile muscles to move the erect penis, either within or outside the vagina. Use this conscious contracting of the penis along with the ejaculatory contractions as they are happening. Then continue conscious contractions for a period of time. Through repeated practice, the involuntary contractions will cease or fade away less readily and the orgasm will be prolonged.

A considerable range of Eastern methods have been developed expressly to enrich and intensify the climactic experience. Works from several of these Asian sources offer both controversial material as well as some new approaches especially those of Mantak Chia (1) Nik Douglas and Penny Slinger (2), as well as (3) David and Ellen Ramsdale's book, *Sexual Energy Ecstasy,* (Bantam, 1994).

PRE-ORGASMIC PLEASURE BALLOON EXTENSION

This exercise, although similar to the climax postponement exercises earlier, has a different focus and purpose. The exercise can be done alone, or it can be used by a couple, with each partner taking turns. (I am indebted for this concept to a therapist, the late Dr. Paul Bindrim of Los Angeles.)

Most men and numerous women are able to distinguish a point during intercourse which marks the very beginning of the progression toward the orgasm. This can be called the *point of onset.*

"It's like a 'click' and I know I'm heading for the Big O.

"Suddenly I can tell it won't be so long until I come."

"Sometime before I reach the 'point of no return,' I'm aware that I am on my way toward orgasm. It's a mounting feeling of pleasurable fullness. I can still slow down and even stop."

Although, from the point of onset to the actual climax, feelings of heightened pleasure or ecstasy can be distinguished, the duration of this *pleasure balloon* is all too brief for the vast majority. This exercise is designed to lengthen or extend this pre-orgasmic pleasure balloon.

Many men and women are aware of their point of onset, while others have never paid any attention to this point because their major focus was on achieving climax. Nothing else mattered. As a result, for some, the orgasm appears to happen suddenly and without warning. "I am having intercourse and suddenly, out of the clear blue, I come." For those men who wish they had longer staying power, this exercise can be of special help. (Note: the point of onset in men is *prior to* ejaculatory inevitability.) Some women are already aware of their point of onset, since they have identified their *orgasm herald,* (see Chapter 7, p.143).

It is best for partners to take turns while using this exercise. The partner who is selected, focuses his or her total awareness on *the point of onset,* mentioning it to the partner when this point is reached. At this point, all movement ceases. (The man may wish to withdraw his penis.) If the man finds himself moving too rapidly toward the orgasm, use the squeeze technique (p. 203) described previously.

After an interval which allows enough time for the erotic excitation to diminish, coital movements are resumed. This process is repeated several times, *always with the concentration on the point of onset (or orgasm herald), which should be mentioned aloud to the partner immediately when it occurs.* It may require 6-8 or more sessions to achieve prolongation of the pre-orgasmic pleasure balloon. The orgasm will also be much more intense when you finally let it happen.

If either of you have difficulty identifying the point of onset, proceed very slowly at the beginning of coitus. Focus full attention on genital feelings as you begin. *Stop after a short time and communicate about your sensations and feelings to the partner.* Then continue.

The exercise can also be done alone. If alone, use a tape recorder to record sensations and feelings. Repeat this process until you identify changes in sensations which herald the onset of the climax. If you are a man and you find yourself moving too rapidly toward orgasm, use the squeeze technique, or others, to diminish erotic excitation of the penis.

THE ORGASM DIARY

Keeping an orgasm diary focuses awareness on what transpires during the course of the climactic process. It also helps in developing orgasm discrimination. It is especially helpful for those who do not have a partner, yet wish to develop and improve the quality of their climax. Use of the orgasm diary will require application of willpower, however, since the tendency after the climax is to relax, rather than to record what just took place.

It is best to write down what happened during the orgasm immediately upon its cessation. *Most people will forget what has just transpired if they do not begin to recall the event at once. It is best not to attempt to analyze or try to understand any of the phenomena as they are being written down or dictated.* This can be done later.

A tape-recorded diary has definite advantages. The voicing of what happened appears to accelerate the development of discrimination between the various elements or segments of the orgasmic process. It also fosters recall. The disadvantage of a tape recording is that it is more difficult to become aware of changes or patterns in the orgasmic content. This largely eliminates obtaining a recognition of gradual progress. An overview of what has transpired over several climactic sessions can be much more easily obtained by glancing over several pages of notes. (An easy solution is to transcribe tape recordings.)

Depending on the individual, the Orgasm Diary can focus on three areas:

1. Images, fantasies, symbols, colors and sequential happenings and the Orgasmic States of Being (Chapter 7, pp. 127-143).

2. The feelings or emotions experienced during the climax.

3. Bodily sensations such as contractions, tinglings, energy surges, feelings of warmth, etc.

At the conclusion of the orgasmic experience, immediately make note of images and fantasies. These are the most fugitive, and most fleeting, and need to be captured on paper or by voice as quickly as possible. Then proceed to feelings and body sensations.

Results come after repeated use of the diary, not skipping a single session. (Skipping a session is like taking two steps back.) It may take 6-8 or more diary entries for positive results to become evident. However, the investment of effort in this exercise is made worthwhile by the development of orgasmic capacities, the emerging of new dimensions of ecstasy and pleasure, as well as new insights and understanding.

The following excerpts are from an Orgasm Diary that was begun by a woman in her late thirties some time after she became aware of the orgasmic state of being called "multidimensional climactic experiencing." Multi-dimensional climactic experiencing is characterized by visions or images of a highly aesthetic nature, usually in color. These beautiful vistas may pulsate with the ecstasy of the orgasm. Occasionally, there may be transcendental feelings or an experience of mystical union during the climax (see Chapter 7, p. 137).

These excerpts have been selected *to reflect forward movement in the multidimensional type of climactic experiencing.* The individual keeping the diary was a professional woman who separates her experience into that of images, feelings and bodily sensations.

June 19, 1987

Images—usual glowing and *alive* colors with carpets of flowers, grass, lichens, etc. Emotional elements connected with my experience of originally "seeing" these flowers were minimal. Did not feel like amplifying any of them because for the first time there was such a strong sense of *textures* that I could almost touch them. It was as if I could feel the various textures of flowers, etc. within my being. Became totally involved in this. The transitional flow from flowers to grass, etc. was, as usual, so smooth I could not notice the movement of transition.

Feelings—total involvement in image flow with feelings of awe, delight, curiosity, being energized.

Body—*long body contractions after pleasure feelings of orgasm had ceased. Strong sense that I must let the body reactions run their course and not interrupt hip movements, etc.*

July 28, 1987

Images—A mystical union after ten or eleven months of none. Seemed to last one tenth of a second coupled with highest ecstasy. Dipped into the *sea of all human emotions happening in the world at that moment* an unbelievably rich, balmy, deep, fecund pool. A very brief float, very hard to describe. A sea of energy yet calm a spectrum of emotions changing, yet the same. A very vitalizing dip. Yearning for more of this sense of great loss that it's gone.

Feelings—awe, peak, ecstasy, happiness followed by deep calm, a sense of communion with partner.

Body—*very* aware of self as a physical process saliva running down from lips, contact with wet flesh, etc. One of the highest total body pleasure peaks.

August 4, 1987

Images—first "viscous" experience rivers of changing green but mostly lower flat colors like flowing plastic or paint. Shapes within the color varying with the pleasure rhythm of the orgasm. Then another green with a different viscous flow. Was completely caught in the newness of it all.

Feelings —high curiosity, interest, involvement.

Body—very long period of *body contractions after pleasure of orgasm ceases.*

August 25,1987

Images—a grape vineyard in a full, vibrant state of sunlight, shimmering with energy, growth and becoming. Different shades of green from light to dark. Clusters of grapes, huge, soft green shading into yellow. A yellow sheen to all clusters. There then appeared a massive symbol growing and expanding in the foreground with vineyard in back.

On my realizing that *I was seeing a symbol (for the first time)* it disappeared. Feelings of both delight and fear at this new breakthrough. Next appeared a human figure on a bare stage of brown boards (black background with gray beams in starkly contrast design). The figure of a young man, still with the boyish fat of childhood, benign and jolly looking. He is taking a few steps, gesturing, saying something. (Can't hear his voice.)

I am intensely aware of this sequence of action. I realize that this is a symbolic thing he is doing. I am again glad and scared about this new challenge. A form of the unconscious communicating something to my conscious self? Maybe this means I am entering a new territory. *Am very pleased I did not try to analyze what it means during the orgasmic image flow, while the orgasm was taking place, as this has always stopped the flow.*

Feelings—fear, joy, amazement, gladness and strong feelings of love.

Body—orgasm lasted unusually long with pleasure feelings (mild) lasting almost to the very end of body contractions. (A new pattern?)

Just as I am writing this, recalled that this orgasmic experience started with a series of dark, threatening symbolic scenes. Sudden images illuminated by stark, somber light. It frightened me and I "wanted away from it." This happened and the vineyard appeared.

I could not recall anything about the shape of the vineyard symbol. Did *not* want to write this entry. Had to force myself using all my willpower. Just wanted to lie and enjoy. But, realized that to do this was a destructive thing. *Feel good that I made myself write.* (Emphasis added.)

The above diary entries seem somewhat more eloquent than usual. However the objective of this exercise is to put down *in your own words,* what has transpired, no matter how halting, simple, lengthy or complex these entries may be, or how they are stated.

G-SPOT ORGASM DEVELOPMENT—SOME SPECIAL CONSIDERATIONS

This section is included because a considerable proportion of women have not made use of the G-Spot as a source of erotic pleasure or orgasm. If this applies to the reader, you are urged to review the material on the G-Spot in Chapter 4, pp. 66-71.

Much about G-Spot sex remains a mystery. This is in part traceable to the fact that two sexologists (Masters and Johnson), widely known for their sex research, have long denied that a G-Spot exists. (For a more detailed history, see

Chapter 4,p. 67). Years later, Masters and Johnson again essentially denied the existence of the G-Spot, in their 1994 book, *Heterosexuality.*

The G-Spot remains somewhat of a mystery because some women do not appear to have this spot. An alternative possibility is that there are women, who for any number of reasons, (conscious or unconscious), are not interested in developing or activating this erotic zone.

Most women need to use firm pressure to stimulate the G-Spot, once it is located. Others prefer gentler pressure, or stroking. The training to develop the capacity for G-Spot sex and the G-Spot orgasm involves the stroking of this spot by the woman herself, or by her partner. Take a gradual approach, using variations in pressure and have at least five to seven stroking sessions to develop erotic sensitivity. (It may take longer, but there are also women who develop sensitivity and orgasm quickly.)

An essential part of G-Spot orgasm development involves talking about it either to oneself or, preferably, to a loving partner. ("This is beginning to feel pleasurable. It feels good.") An alternative is to keep a diary. Write down the feelings, time spent and what happened in detail focusing on attitudes and sensations.

The foremost researcher of G-Spot sex is Dr. Beverly Whipple. She also has noted what interviewees have repeatedly told me. For many women, as the G-Spot begins to be stroked or stimulated, *it feels to them like an urge to urinate.* Numerous individuals cease further stimulation at this point. However, this is usually a passing sensation which only signals that progress is being made.

Persistence during the process of sexual self-development is very much a key principle.

Finally, it must be mentioned that along with the G-Spot orgasm, some women develop the ability to ejaculate. This ejaculate is *not urine,* as numerous tests have repeatedly established. (The process has also been filmed, revealing that some women have an ejaculation similar in strength to that of some men.) It is deplorable that close-minded individuals continue to deny both the existence of the G-Spot and the ejaculatory capability of many women.

Sexological researchers appear to be divided into two camps—the conservatives and the open-minded. Conservative sexologists seem to insist that for a sex phenomenon to exist and merit acknowledgment, it must be present in most, if not all of the subjects studied. They refuse to accept the fact that *the essence of sexual behavior, sexual phenomena and human sexuality lies in the richness of its diversity. Sexual self-development and sensual self-expression are one of humanity's major indicators not only of the species', creativity, but also its capacity for individuation.*

Resources

1. Mantak Chia and Maneewan Chia, *Cultivating Female Sexual Energy,* (1986) and Mantak Chia and Michael Winn, *Cultivating Male Sexual Energy,* (1985). Both are available from Healing Tao Books, 2 Creskill Place, Huntington, NY 11743.

2. Nik Douglas and Penny Slinger, *Sexual Secrets,* (Inner Traditions, 1979).

3. David and Ellen Ramsdale, *Sexual Energy Ecstasy,* (Bantam, 1994).

4. Jack Morin, *Anal Pleasure and Health,* (3rd edition, 1998). Obtainable from Good Vibrations Store, 1210 Valencia Street, San Francisco, CA 94110. ($18.00).

5. Tristan Taormino, *The Ultimate Guide to Anal Sex For Women,* (Cleis Press, 1998).

CHAPTER 12

THE HUMAN ORGASM: EXPLORING THE FURTHER REACHES OF THE POSSIBLE

"The important thing is never to stop questioning."
-Albert Einstein

Many of the preceding chapters have dealt with what the Italian sexologist and philosopher Julius Evola calls "the introspective evidence about the innermost experience of sex." (1) It has been one of the major themes of this volume that sexual self-development, as a life-long adventure, can be an enjoyable pursuit which fosters health and increases *joie de vivre*. In this final chapter, some of the more esoteric concepts and speculations about the human climax are discussed.

The Appendix is entitled "Human Sexuality; Additional Observations and Reflections." (A list of the eleven topics discussed in the Appendix is found on p. 225). It will be of particular interest to those readers for whom their ongoing sexual self-development plays a core role in their life-long growth as a person.

REFLECTIONS ABOUT THE FURTHER REACHES OF THE ORGASMIC POTENTIAL

The orgasm is a creative paradox, since we can develop, shape and form it to a considerable extent, while at the same time, it shapes, forms and develops us.

* * *

The orgasm is becoming an open door to the riches hidden in the infinity of our inner universe.

* * *

The Orgasm is-

a reflection of the many faces of God.

an expression of deep thankfulness to the universe.

a way of delving into the mysteries of ourselves and each other.

a means of quenching and replenishing our appetite for carnal knowledge, one of the most hidden forms of beauty.

a way of experiencing and expressing our deepest emotions to each other.

* * *

Sex and the orgasm are dimensions of the existential quest often visited but least systematically explored and utilized. It can be a most powerful tool in the development of the human psyche and its spiritual and creative capacities.

* * *

The sexual act and the orgasm experienced in the context of healthy, life nurturing mental and emotional attitudes *is the most dynamic and powerful source of generating caring and love for each other as human beings.* This needs to be taught in all elementary, high school and college sex education programs.

* * *

The quickest way to cut through the sham, masks, defenses and barriers between two people is by together pursuing the greatest sexual pleasure of which each is capable.

* * *

The orgasm is both an entering into an ego-less state as well as an exploration and extending of the boundaries of the ego. Once more we are confronted by the human climax as a creative paradox.

* * *

Sex and the experience of the orgasm permeates our emotions, alters the way we feel about ourselves, changes the way we think and affects the way we relate to people.

* * *

A man I interviewed told me that he has "prayer orgasms." He said, "As I climax, I meditate that God and I are one and that my real essence is divine." He stated that his *prayer orgasms* give him more energy and that he feels more fulfilled. I am reminded of my visits to the late Michael Zamorro's Group Mind Commune which flourished in Los Angeles in the mid and late seventies. Varied styles of prayer orgasms were extensively used during couple and group sex in this commune.

Governmental attempts to control what happens sexually, in the privacy of the bedroom between consenting adults, is a most dangerous first step toward total control of the person. If a person can be controlled in the most private precincts of life, that person is more prone to accept control and coercion in other areas of life.

We are living at a time in history when the suppression of sexual freedom through the implementation of sexually repressive laws is at a fairly low ebb. (This, despite the recent U. S. Supreme Court decision prohibiting sodomy between consenting adults in the privacy of their bedroom.)

Sexual energy and the human orgasm are inextricably linked. *The human being has the capacity to create centers of sexual peak ecstacy; centers which can trigger the ograsm.*

This occurred to me as I looked back on my work with the climax spanning a dozen years, while doing the final editing for this book. What triggered this line of thought was an observation about the male of the species. The male is capable of creating a sexual energy center by using psychological or inner subjective processes to sensitize his anal sphincter area.

The many orgasms men have reported to me as a result of the practice called "rimming" proves that a sensitive energy center was established. The zone orgasm (reported by both genders), where the side of the neck, fingers and other zones are sensitized, making a climax possible, is another example of this phenomena.

It is now my hypothesis that this capacity to create sexual centers, which trigger orgasms, can be learned. This discoveery will have vast implications, with eventual profound effects on the social fabric of our society.

What really goes on during the orgasm?

Hope is nourished. (There is more where that came from)

The ego gets a gentle stroke.

The importance of the sexual aspects of our being is reaffirmed.

The god and goddess are given the chance to recognize and meet.

Spirits touch and tendrils of tenderness and love are nourished.

Connectedness with the ALL is reaffirmed.

Shame and fear are likely to be purged.

The sex muscles are exercised.

There appears to be a need to both minimize and maximize the importance of what is going on.

We don't want to admit to ourselves how profoundly we are being moved.

We make love and love makes us.

We celebrate being a man and a woman and being human.

We learn to flow with life.

The music of the bodies is rediscovered.

There is a shocking revelation of rhythm as a basic life *force.*

We have the sometimes gut knowledge that this is a path of spiritual evolution.

We now have the pleasure of choice plus many options about our orgasms. Developing them can be a new form of play that will yield ever expanding qualities of ecstasy.

From my notebooks:
The orgasm has an infinity of faces. Today, for the first time is a very new experience. In the beginning of the orgasm, there was a very faint sensing, a feeling, (a whiff) of *thankfulness.* Pursuing this sensing, there came waves of profound thankfulness becoming ever deeper and broader.
At the same time, there was an increase in the strength and dimensionality of erotic pleasure—the pleasure had a more profound, beautiful, textured "taste." It was a spiritual experi-

ence.   The feelings of thankfulness were like an adoration. The realization came that an orgasm can open the door to spiritual experiences *other* than the mystical union.   It was a shaking insight.

I had not thought myself capable of such intensity of spiritual experiencing—like a revelation.   I had the realization that much more is possible.   The orgasm operates like an energy stream flowing into directions toward which we can channel it.   I had let it flow in the direction of sensing a feeling of thankfulness.

In the 21st century, sex and the orgasm will be recognized and utilized as fulcrum forces in the ongoing development and growth of the human personality and its latent powers and possibilities.

The process of exploring the bountiful riches inherent in the human orgasm also keeps alive and nourishes the capacity for curiosity.   Curiosity is a primal force in the human personality.   Diminishing or the expiring of curiosity deadens the enjoyment of life and will to live of the organism.   In this context, orgasm development with a focus on nourishing *sexual curiosity* both energizes and sustains human survival.

* * *

As I came into a better understanding of the orgasm, I began to realize that it functions as a gateway. It not only offers a door to the enlarging of our self-knowledge, but even more important, the orgasm both generates and partakes of an energy field which connects us to those larger powers which beckon for union and which are the Ground of our Being. Finally, the orgasm invites us to become psychonauts in the exploration and shaping of our inner universe.

* * *

During the annual 1998 meeting in Los Angeles of the Society For The Scientific Study Of Sexuality, author, publisher and sexologist Ray Stubbs made a very interesting presentation entitled "A Mystical View of the Orgasm." He distinguishes between the Physical Body sexual orgasm, the Essence Center Astral Orgasm, the Spirit Body energetic orgasm and the Light Body full body orgasm. I am looking forward to his further work in this area.

* * *

I am convinced that the orgasm has healing properties. How this healing energy can be developed and focused will be discovered on the first third of the new millenium. At that time every one will know that sex can function as a healing force.

* * *

The importance of knowing that we can play with and shape our orgasms cannot be overestimated. We become more creative on the most intimate level of our being. The orgasm becomes a creative process and this nurtures life-affirmative forces, thereby strengthening the will to live.

The findings presented in this volume describe a multitude of ways to liberate the orgasm. The liberated orgasm presents each person who is capable of accepting this framework with multiple creative opportunities. This work has also resulted in a fresh approach to the exploration and development of the many dimensions of an empowered spectrum of peak ecstatic experiencing. A reassessment of the components of the human sexual nervous system has also begun to emerge.

New information about the species' capacity for peak ecstatic experiencing has been generated, fueling the orgasmic revolution. Among the greatest gifts of such new knowledge is that it stimulates and encourages us to deepen and extend the horizons of our self-understanding, while at the same time opening new avenues toward a better understanding of our contemporaries.

It is a major outcome of this study to offer ways and means by which men and women can take charge of their own orgasm to greatly expand, shape and enrich it, if they so desire. This is a part of the erotic awakening of humanity which began during the sexual revolution of the sixties, and which is still only in its beginnings.

ADDENDUM

It is my conclusion, reached in the seventh decade of this life, that our sexuality remains one of the great mysteries of this existence. It has long been used by ruling elites (governments) to control humanity. This, in order to limit and suppress our capacity to love ourselves, each other and this planet. The restriction of sexual freedom (through laws, the censoring and restriction of information, plus the instilling of destructive belief systems about sex) has had an effect unknown to most.

It has kept us from the active and dedicated pursuit of unfolding our sexual as well as our spiritual potential. It has kept us from experiencing the depth and intensity of spiritual search and communion of which we are capable. *Hidden in sex is the specie's capacity to generate love.* Any new information about human sexuality can strengthen this capacity and enable us to become more loving beings. It is from this perspective that *Liberated Orgasm* is offered to the public.

Notes

1. Julius Evola, *The Metaphysics of Sex,* (Inner Traditions, International, 1983): 5.

HUMAN SEXUALITY: ADDITIONAL OBSERVATIONS AND REFLECTIONS

"... the most adaptive development in the evaluation of our own species seems to have been the development of our great human capacity for love, and not, as some earlier theorists claimed, our capacity for great violence and aggression."

Riane Eisler

This Appendix includes discussion of the following topics:

- A major American challenge

- The great unacknowledged scandal in the sex life of the U.S.

- The medical uses of sex as a healing agent

- Creating the first World Museum of Erotic Literature & Art

- Sex toxicity a hidden international plague

- A puzzling question

- The man in the woman and the woman in the man

- Man, sex and society

- Christianity and sex

- What few dare ask themselves

- About non-relational sex and the expression of loving feelings

- Some additional observations

A major American challenge

More than any other nation, researchers in the United States have added to our knowledge about sex. We must not forget that this type of knowledge considerably helps to expand and increase the sexual pleasure of people in other nations. In a very real sense, this helps make the world a better place to live.

In view of this, it is all the more surprising to find that there is no fully endowed chair in sexology at any university in America. *This fact speaks* to the nation's ongoing love/hate relationship with sex. The Kinsey Institute is what its name implies—an institute for sex research which is both a repository and memorial to Alfred Kinsey, who died a Professor of Biology.

An endowed chair in sexology (plus adequate research funds) would furnish new impetus and the leadership to stimulate much needed research. It is very clear to specialists in the field that a great deal remains to be discovered about the orgasm and human sexuality. The location of the endowed chair in California would take advantage of the state's permissive social climate, providing a needed dynamic momentum.

Sex will play a much more central role in the lives of people in the future than it does today. The ground swell of sexual diversity will peak in the next few decades. Major gains in sex communication have been made in the latter part of this century. We are on the very threshold of major discoveries about the transformative powers of sexual energy. More than ever before, a major donor is needed who has the vision to see that sex research nourishes the quality of human loving and helps establish a more caring society.

The great unacknowledged scandal in the sex life of the United States

One of the healthiest things people can do in their advanced years is to continue to express their love and affection through intercourse and orgasm. Although I probably will not see it in my lifetime, some of the elder homes of tomorrow will display the following poster: "LOVING ORGASMS FOSTER HEALTH." As a result of leading healthier sex lives, people will live longer in homes for seniors.

Today, in nursing and retirement homes throughout the U. S., management and the staff prohibits the overt display of affection and sexual interest of those living in such facilities. The practice of denying seniors the freedom of sexual expression is a way of hastening older people into early senility and death. The suppression of the sexuality of the aged in such institutions is the most insidious aspect of age discrimination it is the great UNACKNOWLEDGED SCANDAL in the sex life of the United States. An organization is needed to combat this destructive institutional climate.

The medical uses of sex as a healing agent: the ignoring of an important treatment resource

In a lifetime spent as a professor, therapist, sexologist and student of the human personality and its potentials, I have repeatedly found evidence that the human sexual drive could play an important role in the process of healing. My acquaintance in the late forties and early fifties with the physicians Dunbar and Alexander's monumental pioneering work in the area of psychosomatic medicine, plus my meeting the physician Franz Alexander (often called the "father" of psychosomatic medicine), sparked an enduring interest in this area.

It has become ever clearer, since then, that the *unconscious meanings of the disease or injury, linked with emotional factors and the belief system of the patient, are at the core of*

225

both the dis-ease and the healing process. The powerful dynamics of human sexuality vis-a-vis healing and recovery from
trauma and disease are totally neglected by today's medical
profession. The selective use of sex and physical affection,
i.e., body touching, sensual or erotic massage, plus intercourse
and the orgasm *as an integral part of treatment, recovery (and
rehabilitation) programs awaits courageous research-oriented pioneers.* Work in this area will gain rapid momentum in the
years ahead.

What much of today's orthodox medicine is doing to the
belief system and sexual potential of male and female para-
and quadriplegics is deeply destructive to both the psyche
and future sex lives of the patients involved. This specialized
field of medicine is badly in need of a fresh approach for its
rehabilitative programs. There is now evidence that some
spinal cord injured women, who have no sensations in their
genital area, are able to eroticize other parts of their bodies.
*They are capable of having an orgasm from stimulation of these
eroticized parts. The* outstanding pioneering research of sexologists Dr. Beverly Whipple and B. R. Komisaruk in this area
is especially relevant. Undoubtedly men also have a similar
capacity.

Creating the first World Museum of Erotic Literature and Art

Who will do this and thus reap international fame and
the thanks of humanity? We are overdue in establishing the
first World Museum of Erotic Literature and Art. The writer
presented a paper on this subject at the first World Pornography Conference held in Los Angeles in August, 1998. (1) Over
the past five years, erotic literature has emerged as a new
genre, now widely recognized by American publishers, with
dozens of volumes published over the past four years. It is
high time that such literature, like any other type of literature, is recognized as an art form.

*As I have mentioned, more than any other country, the U.
S. has been foremost in its contributions to people's understand-
ing of human sexuality.* Establishing the World Museum of
Erotic Literature and Art would add a much needed, impor-

226

tant dimension. It should probably be located in California, a state known for its openness to new ideas.

The premier pioneers in the area of erotic art were Drs. Eberhard and Phyllis Kronhausen. This brilliant team of U. S. sexologists published a series of trenchant studies about erotica. They were also the founders of the International Museum of Erotic Art which, in the sixties, was briefly open in San Francisco. (It was closed due to economic and political pressure.)

Throughout the history of Western societies, erotic art has been hidden and sequestered in museums not accessible to the public but enjoyed by the nobility and ruling elites of all countries. Rembrandt's erotic paintings still remain to be displayed to the public. Similarly, the beautiful erotic paintings of such artists as the Italian Anibale Caracci and the Russian Count Michael Zichy have never been openly displayed. A complete edition of one of the greatest masters of erotic drawings, Marquis Francis de Bayros has never been published.

Much of the art which has celebrated sex over the past 300 years is of surpassing beauty. However it continues to be banished and concealed. The time has come to bring together a central collection of these important works which celebrate human sexuality and to make them accessible. The individual(s) with the vision to support and create the World Museum of Erotic Literature and Art will be internationally acknowledged *as a visionary who bestowed a great gift to humanity.* He or she (or they) will have the thanks and gratitude of many generations yet to come.

The world museum could bear 'the name of the donor(s) who would endow it. Another possibility is to interest a major college or university in this proposal. My paper, entitled "The World Museum of Erotic Literature and Art" describes this project. I look forward to donating my own very modest collection of erotic literature and contemporary art. I also look forward to devoting the necessary time to help make this project one of America's outstanding and much needed contributions to the world. The interested reader is invited to correspond.

Do *you* know the man or woman who will have instant world fame and the thanks of humanity (for endowing the World Library and Museum of Erotic Literature and Art)?

Sex toxicity—a hidden international plague

Sex toxicity is one of the leading hidden plagues which infest the sex life of the U. S. (and Western) couples, and which considerably limits the pleasure of sex. Its concealed nature greatly contributes to the virulence of this attitudinal dis-ease. Sex toxicity is the equivalent of a psychological pollutant which restricts and blunts erotic enjoyment. Almost everyone in Western societies is to some degree afflicted with a measure of sex toxicity.

The elimination taboos and body secretion taboos are the single most important components contributing to sex toxicity. The transmission of parental attitudes about shit, piss and sex secretions plays a major role. Much of this transmission is non-verbal, making it more powerful.

Body waste taboos form attitudes that impede sexual functioning. Chains of association and the "halo effect" (feelings about one area carried over to a related area or function) play an important role in the process. Beginning with the standard attitude that human waste products are "filthy" or "bad," the organs and apertures involved in elimination become, by association, indecent and "dirty."

Since intercourse involves the production of secretions and involves organs close to and closely associated with elimination, these (innocent) organs become "bad," "shameful," and "indecent." Consequently, again, by association, intercourse and sex play become "dirty." This chain of association is still strongly operative in about 90% of the U. S. population.

The "dirtiness" of sex is universally accepted and is rarely challenged. A magazine supposedly as enlightened as *Redbook* reviewed *The Janus Report* in its March, 1993 issue. Their report stated that "58% of men and women believed that talking dirty is very normal or right."

Conclusions reached in 1972 and published in my book *Total Sex,* continue to be relevant:

"It is time to begin to treat our "natural functions" as *natural*. They underscore the fact that we are part of nature and that we are participants in nature. We must stop our unnatural ways of treating our natural functions. Defecation and all our bodily secretions are a normal, healthy process within the process we call a person.

We are taught that our "shit stinks" and that our bodily secretions "smell bad." The facts are, human elimination greatly varies in smell. Sometimes, if we are honest, we admit it has a pleasing smell. Most of the time it smells *interesting* because it tells us something about ourselves (such as whether certain foods are good for us or not), or it tells us something about our state of health and well-being.

Are we really prepared to continue to foster the myth and illusion that our elimination "smells bad," that our body odors and secretions are "bad," 365 days a year, thus continuously giving ourselves *negative inputs?* Or can we begin to *notice the differences in odors and not label them?"* (2)

There are, however, some clear indications of changes currently taking place in this country. According to an extensive study completed in 1996, American families have made a major change in the toilet training of young children. Over the past decade, children who were formerly toilet trained at age two, are now being trained at age three to three and a half. This, along with the practice of leaving the bathroom door open (or removing it altogether) will contribute significantly to an increase in people's sexual enjoyment.

A puzzling question
I am most thankful for sex humor. We don't put enough humor into sex. Sex and humor go together like ducks and water. The humor in sex makes for a greater appreciation of the comedy of existence.

In October, 1988, sexologist Dr. Carolyn J. Long and I completed a book entitled *Real Life Sex Humor—The First Collection*. This is the first such collection of actual humorous incidents from people's sex lives obtained through interviews. The reaction of publishers to this quite funny collection has been to ignore this work totally. Despite many efforts, we have so far not been able to find a publisher for Volume I of the collection although several years back, humorous sex joke collections were available with such titles as *Extremely Gross Jokes, Truly Tasteless Jokes, etc.*

All of these collections were totally explicit in language and sold very well. However, they heavily emphasized ethnic and other stereotypes, with sections on French, Italian, African-American, Jewish and Polish sex jokes, as well as jests about the handicapped, aged, etc., denigrating these groups. This emphasis undoubtedly contributed to the total decline of this genre. This leaves us with the question: "Why are so many editors and publishers of today uninterested in, if not opposed, to-the actual (and real) humor in people's sex lives?"

The Man in the Woman and the Woman in the Man

It has been my observation that working with the concept of "the man in the woman and the woman in the man" on a sexual/emotional level can bring major positive change to orgasm quality and intensity. I would not be surprised if it also is a key for extending the orgasm spectrum from mono and poly-orgasmic to the hetero-orgasmic state. What I wrote in *Total Sex* in 1972 is still pertinent today.

"The people who have most totally 'bought' the social definition of man and woman are compelled to deny *the man in the woman and the woman in the man* most strongly. Yet myths throughout the ages have dealt with the fundamental unity of the male and female principle.

Plato retold the myth, ancient in his time, that man and woman long ago were one organism, combining the characteristics of both genders, who are now compelled to seek each other in an effort to resume this union."

The gods and goddesses of many religious faiths throughout history were depicted as combining male and female
sex characteristics. Many sexologists and behavioral scientists today recognize a feminine and masculine part to
every human being.

Freud once said: "Generally speaking, every human
being oscillates all through his life between heterosexual
and homosexual feelings, and any frustration or disap-
pointment in the one direction is apt to drive him over
into the other." If we accept Freud's observation, then we
need to accept an element of "homosexuality" in all of us.
From the perspective of holistic sex, it would be much
more accurate to say that *every man or woman has both
feminine and masculine feelings, components, or selves,
which need to find periodic birth or expression."(2)*

I have added the words "need to" in the last sentence of
the previous quotation. This is based on repeated observations over the more than twenty-year period since this book
(Total Sex), was published. I have seen many sexually sophisticated men and women, as the years pass, deny the components of the other gender which exist within them. Inevitably, they do this to their peril. *Denying the expression of aspects of the sexual self is a form of stifling or suppression of
emotional forces which, with time, has a deleterious effect on
the sex life.*

Carl G. Jung's concepts of the anima and animus are
another expression of this same idea. So is the Jungian ana-
lyst June Singer's work related to androgyny. Singer has this
clear one sentence definition: "Androgyny refers to a specific
way of joining the 'masculine' and 'feminine' aspects of a single
human being." (3)

The man especially needs to work through the clusters
of emotional forces currently identified as being related to the
other gender, forces which are hidden within him. Becoming
involved in this process resolves inner/unconscious forces
which are in conflict. The result is a new synthesis as well as
an increase in the flow of energy— specifically sex energy.

The latter now becomes available for fueling personal/sexual growth as well as creativity. *The liberated orgasm concept, by freeing the man from the belief that he is capable only of a penile climax, fosters this whole process.*

The late author, friend and sexologist Adelaide Bry wrote the following for me when we talked about this concept.

"Hidden underneath the set of genitals one happens to be born with are all the emotions and attitudes of the opposite sex. Whether these emotions and attitudes are expressed or repressed depends upon how willing the person is to look at his own opposite.

From my own sex life a man being willing or unwilling to have me be on top. A man being willing or reluctant or even resistant to listening to my sexual needs. A man somewhat afraid of his own sexuality who always wanted to be IN CONTROL. (A sexologist is one who has made his sexual curiosity legitimate.)

Somehow with one man I felt uncomfortable being on top. My mind said he won't like this: I thoroughly enjoyed the power of being on top, and experienced as well the energy required by the man. I could feel what it might be like to always be the man, and having to perform, and thought how happy I was that I could do it when I wanted.

Another time with a man I was surprised that it was so all right with him. I could sense that he didn't mind a bit, and I was more relaxed in the "male" position than I had ever been. For a moment, I fantasized my having a penis and what that would be like, and I thought of how men have taken that thrusting power out into the world to be as powerful as they are.

And then conversely the other that when they do not have their erection, so subtle, so scary when it vanishes, that this power may be like so much in life, tenuous at best, and a power without as much substance as it would seem.

The power to ask and receive is indeed a power long denied to women, and I, myself, despite all my freedoms in my own life, have often not felt truly comfortable in asking, but only in receiving what was offered ... that is the woman in the woman ... in my lexicon."

The concepts of the man in the woman and the woman in the man are particularly offensive to two types of people. They are the macho male, plus those individuals who closely identify themselves with the culturally identified gender related roles.

These people derive a large measure of their sense of identity and selfhood from the cultural (or traditional) definition of what a man is and how he should behave (as a man), and what a woman is and how she should behave (as a woman).

Cultural sex role stereotypes can act as a major impediment to the full enjoyment and development of the individual's sexual potential and human potential.

The great influence of religious conservatism and fundamentalism in the U.S. is associated with the large pool of guilt which appears to underlie the American psyche, and which influences sexual experiencing. This guilt is significantly fueled by the untrammeled materialistic greed which is gutting our planet. At the same time this greed is accelerated by our addiction to violence as a form of entertainment. At the core of the guilt structure lies the recognition that we are not as loving and caring to our environment and fellow human beings as we need to be to assure survival of the species.

Man, Sex and Society

It has been one of society's major myths to keep the man chained to the penile orgasm. By keeping sex in "short supply" and <u>by denying him the actualizing of his sexual potential, the male has historically been kept more (latently) angry and aggressive</u>. At the same time, sexual insecurities and uncertainties of the male have also made him more ready to long for and accept authority, to wage war and, after appropriate training, to readily accept death in battle.

The male of the species appears to have a much greater pool of deep-seated, unacknowledged doubts and insecurities about his sexual functioning than the female. The exposed nature of his sexual equipment, to some extent, provides a basis for this. However, a more fundamental basis for this insecurity appears traceable to the fact that the male erection is not within a man's conscious control. A limp penis while making love is an ever-present potential handicap which spells "danger" and generates insecurity.

I believe, however, that a training sequence will likely be discovered and developed some time in the first part of the 21st century. It will give the man the capability to use his mind, or will, to bring about an erection. Another possibility, of course, is chemical or herbal solutions for this problem, such as the drug Viagra.

Within the last three decades, sex has become much more accessible and user-friendly in this country and other parts of the world. This continuing development, along with the healing of the AIDS epidemic, will provide the much-needed socio/cultural basis for bringing a considerably deeper level of sexual security and sense of well-being to the psyche, especially of the male (as well as female) of the species.

Christianity and sex

As mentioned in previous chapters, there has been a growing interest, particularly in the U.S. (and also Europe), in the spiritual or transcendental aspects of sex and the orgasm. Within recent years, there has been a resurgence of interest by theologians as to the meanings of sexual intercourse from the Judeo-Christian perspective. To stimulate interest in further exploration of this area, especially by couples who may want to discuss these concepts, the following fragments from theological concepts are offered:

- If God is a form of love, then loving (in the act of sexual union) partakes of God in a special way.

- The sexual union is an act of communion with God.

- Intercourse is a joyful celebration of the Lord.

- The sexual union is a form of sacrament or can be such.

- Sex is God's idea, not man's. Sex is a gift of God, and like all other things God made, it has the design of the Creator in it. Sex is not an accident.

- Sex is God. This is the first basic fact that must be completely recognized.

- Sex in itself is good, being a work of Creation. It is, however, used by people who are evil. But this does not make sex evil.

- The Christian views sex as being part of his total personality and part of a total context of life.

- The sexual union is one of the ways we "act out" and express our desire for unity with God.

- "Joy is the most infallible sign of the presence of God." Teilhard de Chardin. (Sexual joy would be included.)

What few dare ask themselves

One of the greatest challenges in life is one of the least recognized. Major cultural and religious proscriptions militate against recognition and acceptance of this challenge. The challenge is triggered by using two key questions:

1) "Where or in what area of my ongoing sexual development should I use courage and willpower to stimulate an increase in lust, desire and passion?"

2) "At this point in my life, what can I do sexually to expand the horizon of my sexual experiencing, thus actualizing more of my sexual pottential?"

These questions are rarely asked. Most people seem to

235

feel that lust and passion are sufficiently present, while opportunities for sexual self-expression are in short supply. However it is also clear that in the absence of passion, relationships become less alive, less vital and loving.

On addressing this question to themselves, many persons have a clear recognition of what they can do to foster their sexual passions. The next step, taking action, is usually never taken. Why is the *ongoing* process of fostering lust, passion and desire so important? *It is a linking with the primal life force which deeply nourishes and sustains the organism.* This process will also ultimately enhance the flow and the juices of creativity. Finally, desire, lust and passion, when translated into action, nourish the will to live, promote health and fuel ecstasy and the celebration of life.

About non-relational sex and the expression of loving feelings

There appears to be an increasing tendency in the U.S. to have "casual sex." In this context sexual desire is usually identified as lust and the sex act is not seen as building or forming an emotional attachment, or relational intimacy. Thus, sexual congress becomes an essentially narcissistic event with participants engaged in non-relational sex. It appears to be largely practiced by men although some women have begun to enter this domain. A key characteristic of this type of sex is the ignoring or suppression of feelings other than erotic sensations. In short, non-relational sex is an option, which, for some, becomes an essential choice, if not a compulsion.

It is undeniable, however, that, for most people, having sex generates feelings of tenderness, caring as well as affection and love. It is important to be aware of and to accept these feelings fully and to communicate how one feels. It is our partner's responsibility to express what she/he feels. The experiencing and communication of caring and loving feelings enhances and strengthens life while increasing our capacity to enjoy existence.

In May, 1997, President Clinton set a ten-year deadline for the defeat of AIDS. This occurred at a time when specialists predicted that a way of effectively dealing with the epidemic could be expected in the near future. Removal of the AIDS threat will inevitably trigger a renaissance in sexual relations, both in the U. S. and other countries. A very significant increase in sexploration and sexual self-development will also take place.

Some additional observations ...

To aim the orgasm toward the heights of its perfection, all pleasure centers of the body need to be explored to determine the peak pleasure of which each is capable. It is like tuning the instruments of a symphony except here the process (of exploration) is more important because it can lead to a promising outcome.

* * *

Western cultures and societies have structured their institutions to keep members from feeling both the *range of erotic ecstasy and the love* of which human beings are capable. *There exists a cultural conspiracy to suppress such feelings.* We are forced to deny this fact because to accept it would lead to a recognition of how totally conditioned by society and its norms we really are. (Furthermore, we do not want to face how hard it is to reverse this process.)

* * *

The truly free person is always at war with the moralizers, inquisitors and censors of the human sexual connection.

* * *

On October 23, 1997, a major breakthrough in neuroscience was heralded by this front-page headline: STUDY OF RATS FINDS SEX CAN CHANGE BRAIN. University of California, Berkeley psychology professor Marc Breedlove discovered that the brain cells controlling movement in male rats could be changed by altering their sexual behavior. (He said) . . .

237

"these findings give us proof for what we theoretically know to be the case—that sexual experience can alter the structure of the brain, just as genes alter it. It is possible that differences in sexual behavior cause, rather than are caused by, differences in brain structure." (4) Emphasis added.

* * *

Sex and erotic pleasure can play an especially important role in helping patients to both regenerate their will to live, and to nourish their enjoyment of life.

* * *

According to a number of surveys of national values, a population's increasing exposure to education usually results in marked gains in sexual permissiveness and open communication about erotic matters. Largely as a result of this process, *sexual pleasure has begun to emerge as a person's birthright, in the recognition that sex is necessary both for people's psychological and physical health.*

Notes

1. Herbert A. Otto, "The World Museum of Erotic Literature and Art," paper presented at the World Pornography Conference, August 6-8, 1998, Universal City, California.

2. Herbert A. Otto and Roberta Otto, *Total Sex,* (Peter Wyden, 1972): 262-263.

3. June Singer, *Androgyny,* (Anchor Books/Doubleday, 1977): 8.

4. "Study of Rats Finds Sex Can Change Brain," *Los Angeles Times,* October 23, 1997: A1, A26.

INDEX

A

accelerated orgasmic intensity process, 44
AFE Zone, 120
Alexander, Franz, 225
Alzate, Heli, 52, 66
American sex attitudes research, 39
Amore, Dante (Paradise Electro Stimulations Company) 147
anal orgasm
    in females 71-77
    in males, 92
Anand, Margo, *The Art of Sexual Ecstasy, 165* anal pump squeeze, 158
anima (Jung), 93, 231
Ann, Chua Chee (Anterior Fornix Erotic Zone-AFF), 120-121
anolingus, 92, 95
associated recall, 192

B

Barbach, Lonnie, *For Each Other, 69, 78*
Becker, Robert O., *The Body Electric, 147*
Ben-wa sex toy, 54
Berry, John, 78
Bindrim, Paul, 206
Bolling, David, 74
Brauer, Alan and Donna
    Extended Sexual Orgasm,
    The ESO Program, 150-152
breast orgasm
    in females, p. 58-59
    in males, 96-99
Bowder, Sue, 131
Bry, Adelaide, 232

C

casual sex, 236
Change, Steven, *The Tao of Sexology, 204*
Chartham, Robert, 96
Chia, Mantak and Arava, Douglas,
    The Multi-Orgasmic Man, 85, 166, 206

C (continued)

child's climax, 116-117
climax (or orgasm) principal components, 139-141
clitoral orgasm, 45-51
clitoridectomy (clitoral circumcision), 49
Colette, 122
conscious orgasm power shift, 152-153
contemporary myths
    about sex, xv, 5
    about clitorocentrism, 18, 45, 67
cul-de-sac response, 121

D

Dalahashvili, Dr. Semyon, 153
de Graaf, Regnier, 66
Dickinson, Robert, 66
Dodson, Betty, 117
Douglas, Nik and Slinger, Penny, *Sexual Secrets, 206*
double penetration, 122
dream orgasms, 113-114

E

Einstein, Albert, 215
Eisler, Riane, 223
ejaculation
    in females, 1, 67
    premature, in males, 87
Elk, Lightning, Rainbow, Stephanie, 160
Ephros, P., 167
erection (penile), 87
erotic and sexual literature, 7
Evans, Michael, 67
Evola, Julius, Metaphysics of Sex, 156, 215

F

fellatio, 101
Female prostatic ejaculation, 126
Feuerstein, Georg, *Sacred Sexuality, 156*
Freud, Sigmund, 55
fusion (or blended) orgasm, 107-110
training in, 193-195
Friday, Nancy, *Women On Top, 74*

G

Garfield, Patricia, *Paths to Ecstasy, 114*
Gogokhia, Dr. S, 153
Grafenberg, Ernst, 66
G-Spot orgasm, 66-71,213
    training in, 212-213

H

Hartman, William and Fithian, Marilyn, *Any Man Can,* 85, 99
Heidenry, John, *What Wild Ecstasy,* 66
hetero-orgasmic defined, 16, 22-23, 49
hierarchic tendency, 12
Hite, Shere, 5, 47
Hoch, Zwi, 51
Homosexuality/Lesbian Sexual Study, 148-150
human sexual nervous system, 14-15

I

intercourse and orgasm belief system, 11, 28-30
    effects of, 34-38
    restructuring, 37
intercourse, frequency of, 4

J

James, William, 38
Janus Report, 1993, 36, 228
Journal of Sex Research, 178
Jenks, Richard J., 10
Jung, Carl G., 231

K

Kaplan, Helen S., 44
Keesling, Barbara, *Super Sexual Orgasm,* 121
Kegel, Arnold, 146
Kline-Graber, Georgia and Graber, Benjamin, 146
Kinsey, Alfred
    findings, 114, 125, 224
    woman's mental orgasm, 77
    orgasm definition, 125
Komisaruk, Barry, 77

K (continued)

Kronhausen, Eberhard and Phyllis, 227

L

LaBerge, Stephen, *Lucid Dreaming*, 114, 115
Ladas, Perry and Whipple
    climax and orgasm distinction, 3
    clitoris, 47
    A-frame effect, 51
    The G-Spot, 91
    fusion orgasm, 108
Landers, Ann, 174
Lao Tzu, 158
Lester, Harold, 102
liberated orgasm, xv
resistance to, 26-28
training in, 151-152
Liberating Creations, xvi,
Lightfoot-Klein, Hanny, 48-49
LoPiccolo, Joseph, *Handbook of Sex Therapy*, 43-44
Long, Carolyn J., 230
lucid dream orgasm,8, 114-116

M

Magical Blend A Transformative Journal, 155
marijuana, use of, 178
Masters, William and Johnson, Virginia, 11, 45-46, 126, 212-213
Masters, Johnson and Kolodny, Robert, *Heterosexuality*, 67
masturbation
    couples, 189
    climax through, 117-119
McCrary, James, *Human Sexuality*, 96
McIlvenna, Ted, 154
Mead, Margaret, *Male and Female*, 2
Meldmans, Louis, *Mystical Sex-love, Ecstasy and the Mystical Experience*, 156
mental orgasm
    in females, 77-81
        from external stimuli, 79-80
        inner-directed, 80-81
    in males, 102-104

M (continued)

Meshorer, Marc and Judith, *Ultimate Pleasure*, 78-82
Metaphysics of sex, 156
mono-orgasmic, 17
    defined, 17
Money, John, xv, xvi
Morin, Jack, *Anal Pleasure and Health*, 74, *The Erotic Mind*, 160
Mosher, Donald, 126
mouth orgasm
    in females, 61-65
    in males, 99-102
multiple orgasm
    in females, 41-44
    in males, 86-88

N
Non-relational Sex, 236

O
Offit, Avodah, *The Sexual Self*, 44, 55
Ogden, Gina, *Women Who Love Sex*, 77-78
    "thinking off," 78
"Sex And Spirit Survey," 160
oral sex, incidence of, 4
orgasm
    definition, 10
    shaping, 24, 125, 144
    female's continuous or sequential, 43
orgasm body patterns, 142-143
orgasm development programs, 150-152
orgasm discrimination, 189-190
orgasm herald, 143-144
orgasm intensification, 167-182
orgasm spectrum range, 12
orgasm shaping a learning process, 132-139
Orgasm Spectrum Research Project, 9
    basic findings 11-18
    participants, 10
    process, 9
    purpose, 8, 9
    half completed, 127

O (continued)

life style influence, 145
orgasm tone, 141-142
    experience (training) 204-212
    orgasmic potential
    focus of study, 8
orgasms, historic three, 5
    developmental nature of, 7
    climactic options, 11-18
Orgasmic Range Survey, 10
orgasmic states of being survey, 1, 15, 27, 127-144
Otto, Herbert A., *Total Sex,* 228-230
Otto, Herbert and Long Carolyn, J., *Real Life Sex Humor The First Collection, 230*

P

Pearsall, Paul, *Sexual Healing,* 145, 147, 154
penile orgasm, 85-89
perineum, 92
polyamory, 165
poly-orgasmic (defined), 17, 23, 112
Pope Paul II, *Family Guide to Sex,* 118
Pomerdy, Wardell, 102
premarital sex, incidence of, 4
prostate orgasm, 89

R

Rajneesh, Bhagwan Shree, 43-44, 119
Ramsdale, David and Ellen, *Sexual Energy Ecstasy,* 146, 206
Reinisch, June, Kinsey Institute New Report, 75
rimming, 92
Robbins and Jensen, 84
Rosenblatt, Roger, 18

S

Scantling, Sandra, *Ordinary Women, Extraordinary Sex,* 131
Schnarch, M. David *Constructing The Sexual Crucible,* 154, 160, 184
seminal fluid, 86
Sevely, Josephine L., *Eve's Secrets, 125*
sex education
    findings, applications, 17
sexploration, 161

S (continued)
Judeo-Christian, 166
Native American, 159-160
sexual belief system, 28-34
sexual health, 153-154
sexual lifestyles and climactic experiencing
homosexual special study, 147-150
sexual potential, 2-3
sexual revolution, 155
sex sandwich (double penetration), 122
sexual self-development, 161-163
sexual secretions, (Tantric beliefs), 158
sex therapy programs
findings, applications, 17-18
Sherfey, Mary Jane, *The Nature And Evolution Of Female Sexuality*, 44
Sholty, Mary Jo, et al, 167
Singer, June, 231
Society for Scientific Study of Sexuality, 92, 220
spiritual dimensions of sex and the orgasm, 155
Stanway, Andrew, 91
Stubbs, Ray, xvi, 220
Swift Deer, Harley, 159
Swingers, 8

T
Tantric Sex rituals, 157, 158
Taoist Sex rituals, 158-159
Tao Te Ching, 158
Taormino, Tristan, *Ultimate Guide to Anal Sex For Women*, 82
Tordjman, Gilbert, 52
Tri-Partite Fusion Orgasm, 108
Twenty-first Century Sex --the Breakthroughs of Tomorrow, 161

U
U-Spot orgasm, 121

V
vaginal/cervical orgasm,51-56
valley orgasm, 159
Vassi, Marco, xv
Viagra, 87

V (continued)

Vienna Institute for Sexual Research
    findings, 77

W

Westheimer, Ruth, *Sex For Dummies*, 93
Whipple, Beverly, xv, 78, 120, 213, 226
Whipple, Beverly et al, study, 80
whole body orgasms, 15, 43, 119-120
World Museum of Erotic Literature and Art, 226-228

Z

Zamorro, Michael group mind commune, 217
Zilbergeld, Bernie, 67
Zwang, G., 47
zone orgasm, 15, 110-113

AUTHOR'S BIBLIOGRAPHY
HUMAN SEXUALITY

Articles, etc.

1. Herbert A. Otto, "Preparing for Sexual Adjustment Before Marriage," Sexology Magazine Vol. XXXIII, No. 8 (March, 1967) pp. 530-552.

2. "Sex and Violence in Contemporary Media; Four Studies," Journal of Human Relations Vol. 16, No. 4 (Fourth Quarter, 1968) pp. 571-589.

3. "Sex and Violence on the American Newsstand," Journalism Quarterly, Vol. XL, No.1, (Winter, 1963) pp. 19-26.

4. "The Pornographic Fringeland on the American Newsstand," Journal of Human Relations, Vol XII, No. 3 (Third Quarter, 1964), pp. 375-390.

5. "How Does An Affair Affect A Marriage?" Sexual Behavior (Sept, 1972), pp. 47-48.

6. "The Otto Pre-Marital Schedules: Three Educational Instruments including the "Sexual Adjustment Schedule" for use in pre-marital counseling. Palo Alto: Consulting Psychologists Press, 1961.

7. Sex Fantasy Sharing" (a group method) and "The Love Life Development Test" in Herbert A. Otto's GROUP METHODS TO ACTUALIZE HUMAN POTENTIAL, Beverly Hills California: Holistic Press, 1975.

8. "Short-term Quality Relationships," Penthouse Forum Vol. 8, No. 4 (Jan 1979, pp. 22-28.

9. Herbert A. Otto, Ph.D., and Irene Gad-Luther, M.D., THE SEXUAL SELF-IMAGE SCALE, Los Angeles, California, Holistic Press, 1979.

10. Herbert A. Otto, "Neues Vom Orgasmus," Sexualmedizin (August, 1988), pp. 464-467.

11. "Topographische Uberlegungen Zum Orgasmus—Neue

11.   "Topographische Uberlegungen Zum Orgasmus—Neue Forschungsergebnisse," in W. Eicher, et al, PRAKTISCHE SEXUAL MEDIZIN, Wiesbaden, W. Germany, Verlag Medical Tribune (1988), pp. 101-108.

12.   "Shooting For The Stars," Hustler Vol. XIV, No. 10 (April, 1989), pp. 30-34.

13.   "New and Improved Orgasm," Penthouse Forum Vol. XVIII, No. 8 (April 1989), pp. 18-26.

Books

1.   Herbert A. Otto, MORE JOY IN YOUR MARRIAGE, New York: Hawthorne Books, Inc. 1969. (Sections on sexual adjustment.)

2.   Herbert A. Otto, Editor, THE NEW SEXUALITY, Palo Alto: Science and Behavior Books, Inc., 1971

3.   Herbert A. Otto and Roberta Otto, TOTAL SEX; New York: Peter H. Wyden, Inc., Publishers, 1972. (Paperback edition-New York: New American Library, Signet (1973).

4.   Herbert A. Otto, Editor, THE NEW SEX EDUCATION, New York: Association Press, 1978.

HOW TO ORDER ADDITIONAL COPIES OF THIS BOOK

Each copy: $23.95
Shipping and handling   3.50
Total: $27.45

Note: California residents add sales tax $1.86. Total becomes
$27.81.

(For 3 or more copies, shipping and handling is free)

If you send a check, you can expect delivery in about 3-4 weeks.

If you send a money order, you can expect delivery in about 10 days.

For priority delivery (approximately 6 days), send a money order for
$23.95 plus $4.00 for priority handling—total $27.95 (California residents add $1.86 sales tax for a total of $29.81)

OVERSEAS ORDERS
(All countries including Canada)
International Money Order only plus $6.00 shipping and handling

Send to:

LIBERATING CREATIONS, INC.
P.O. Box 524
Silverado, CA 92676-0524

Order Form

**LIBERATED ORGASM: $23.95; Shipping & Handling $2.00
(Priority Handling $4.00)**
California sales tax $1.86 (California residents only)
Total Enclosed $_____

Please print

Name: ————————————————————————

Street: ———————————————————— Apt No. ————

City: ———————————— State: ——————— Zip: ——————

ENCLOSURE: Check ——— Money Order ———
(Please mark one)

249